THE SOUL OF THE APE
&
MY FRIENDS THE BABOONS

THE SOUL
OF THE APE
&
MY FRIENDS
THE BABOONS

EUGÈNE MARAIS

A DISTANT MIRROR

WWW.ADISTANTMIRROR.COM.AU

THE SOUL OF THE APE
by Eugène N. Marais
First published in Great Britain by Anthony Blond Ltd, 1969

MY FRIENDS THE BABOONS
by Eugène N. Marais
First published in Great Britain by Blond & Briggs, 1975

This edition © 2018 A Distant Mirror
Edited by David L. Major

ISBN 978-0-9807706-7-4

This book contains the texts of the two titles by Eugène Marais – *The Soul of the Ape* and its companion text, *My Friends the Baboons*. Each title is also available as a separate ebook. See the publisher's web site for details.

By the same author:
The *Soul of the White Ant* is available separately as an ebook and in paperback.

A DISTANT MIRROR

web - adistantmirror.com.au
email - admin@adistantmirror.com.au

Contents

Publisher's Note

Eugène Marais spent three years living in the South African wilderness in close daily contact with a troop of baboons. He later described this as the happiest, most content time of his troubled life. This period produced two works which are testament to his research and conclusions; they have very different histories.

Firstly, there was a series of articles written in Afrikaans for the newspaper *Die Vaderland*. They were then published in book form under the title *Burgers van die Berge,* and were first published in an English translation in 1939 under the title *My Friends the Baboons*. These pieces were written in a popular vein suitable to a newspaper readership, and were not regarded seriously by Marais himself. They are a journal; a series of anecdotes and impressions.

The Soul of the Ape, which Marais wrote in clear and precise English, was the more serious scientific document; however after his death in 1936, it could not be found. It was lost for 32 years, and was recovered in 1968, and published the following year.

The excellent introduction by Robert Ardrey that is included in this volume was part of the 1969 and subsequent editions of *The Soul of the Ape,* and adds greatly to an appreciation of its importance.

Together, these three texts give us as complete a picture as we will ever get of Marais' three year study of these complex relatives of humanity, and its implications for the study of consciousness.

Eugène Marais is also the author of *The Soul of the White Ant,* his exploration of the psyche and social life of the termite. It was always his intention that the two bodies of work, on termites and apes, were companion pieces in the search for an understanding of the psyche that would span the gulf between the insect and primate worlds. The point of Marais' work was, always, the mystery of consciousness itself, on which grounds it is as relevant as ever.

Eugène Marais

EUGÈNE MARAIS, the distinguished South African scientist, lawyer, journalist and poet, was born in a farming community near Pretoria in 1872. Educated in the Transvaal, Orange Free State and Cape Province, he made journalism his first career.

By 1890, he was editor of *Land en Volk*, and two years later, at the age of 21, he owned it. In 1894 he married, only to see his wife die the following the year after the birth of his son. This was a loss from which he never really recovered.

Shortly afterwards, he moved to London where he studied law and medicine. By the time of his admission to the bar at the Inner Temple, the Boer War was in progress, and Marais returned to Africa to assist his countrymen.

In 1910, he went to Johannesburg to establish himself as an advocate, but increasing depression of spirits drove him to retreat to Waterberg, a mountain area in northern Transvaal. Settling near a large group of chacma baboons, he became the first man to conduct a prolonged study of the primates in the wild. It was during this period that he produced *My Friends the Baboons*, and gathered the material for the more scientific *The Soul of the Ape*.

*

My Friends the Baboons is that rare piece of writing; a paper of scientific observation which could reduce anyone of compassion to tears – for who cannot be moved by the final chapter when a tribe of baboons appeals to Marais and his companion to save their young?

Marais, journalist, poet, scholar and scientist, spent more than three years studying the chacma baboons in the wild, and his notes, comments and conclusions in this pioneering work have been a source of inspiration since they were written. At the time he began his work, he was able to study a troop of baboons who had never known man. The four-year Boer War removed the settlers, and the baboon troop led an undisturbed life, with no fear of their modern and most devastating foe: human farmers.

Marais was fortunate in being able to watch this animal society in a natural environment. His observations of what they did and how they organised their lives together, how they expressed themselves, and above all, their 'instinctive' reactions, allowed Marais to draw conclusions on the development of animal and human psyche which caused, and continue to cause, debate in scientific circles, and which are as pertinent today as they ever were.

The keenness of his observations is magnificently matched by his compassionate prose. Even the weight of his conclusions is expressed in language so eloquently moving that the very style of the book makes it a treasure to read and possess.

Doris Lessing wrote in *The New Statesman*:

> "He offers a vision of nature as a whole, whose parts obey different time-laws, move in affinities and linkages we could learn to see: parts making wholes on their own level, but seen by our divisive brains as a multitude of individualities, a flock of birds, a species of plant or beast. We are just at the start of an understanding of the heavens as a web of interlocking clocks, all differently set: an understanding that is not intellectual, but woven into experience. Marais brings this thought down into the plain, the hedgerow, the garden."

*

He returned to Pretoria to practise law, to resume his animal studies, and to write poetry in Afrikaans. (He could write in English, but preferred not to, because of his horror of British behaviour during the Boer War.)

In 1926, the year after he had published a definitive text on his original and ground-breaking conclusions about the white ant, the famous European writer Maurice Maeterlinck stole half of Marais' work, and published it as his own. Out of dignity, Marais refused to sue.

This period of Marais' life is discussed in some detail in Robert Ardrey's introduction.

After years of increasing difficulties with morphine, depression and anxiety, he took his own life in 1936.

Glossary

The following terms used in this book might be unfamiliar.

bushveld – a sub-tropical woodland ecoregion of Southern Africa named after the term veld. It encompasses most of Limpopo Province and a small part of the North West Province of South Africa, the Central and North-East Districts of Botswana and the Matabeleland South, and part of the Matabeleland North provinces of Zimbabwe.

bywoner – a poor white tenant farmer who labours for the owner and does some farming of his own

dagga – the South African term for marijuana or cannabis

dassie – a small, herbivorous mammal in the order Hyracoidea, also known as the rock hyrax

duiker – any of several species of small southern African antelopes of the Cephalophinae subfamily

gwarrie – a shrub whose fruit can be fermented for vinegar

kaffir – a black South African

kaross – a treated animal skin cloak or blanket with the hair still left on

klapper – coconut

klipbuck – a type of deer

kloof – a deep glen or ravine

kop – can have various meanings; in this context it refers to the crest of a rock formation or hill

krans – can have various meanings; in this context it refers to a cliff

kwagga – zebra

makoppa – black mamba snake

mealie – an ear of corn or maize

moepel – a tree which provides an edible fruit

poenskop – a large South African sea bream of shallow waters, which typically has a fleshy bump on the snout

poort – a narrow pass through mountains

spruit – a small watercourse, typically dry except during the rainy season

stad – city, or settlement

stoep – A raised veranda in front of a house

tambotie – Marais describes 'tambotie grass', yet the Tamboti is a medium-sized South African tree

uithoek – backwater; a remote, isolated place that is perceived as primitive, godforsaken or backward

veld – the open grassland of South Africa and neighboring countries

Volksraad – the parliament of the former South African Republic. It existed from 1857 to 1902 in part of what is now South Africa. The body ceased to exist after the British victory in the Second Anglo-Boer War.

Eugène Marais

INTRODUCTION

ROBERT ARDREY

HE WAS a courtly man, gentlemanly in an old-time sense, and handsome according to the traditional definitions of masculinity. We might say today that he possessed 'charisma'. His charm was something that contemporaries who outlived him recall with fondness. His paternal magnetism was that of a Pied Piper of Hamelin – a quality to which we shall return.

But he was also a poet with no eternal page to write upon. As a scientist he was unique, supreme in his time, yet he was a worker in a science as yet unborn. He was a freak, spawned by the exuberance of mankind, an immortal who speaks to us from the grave: Beware and do likewise.

*

Eugène Marais was a human community in the person of one man. He was a poet, an advocate, a journalist, a story-teller, a drug addict, a psychologist, and a natural scientist.

He embraced the pains of the many, the visions of the few, and perhaps the burden was too much for one man. But perhaps, also, none but such a human community in one man could have written, almost half a century ago, *The Soul of the Ape*. This manuscript, which was lost for so long, must rank today as a significant contribution to a science that did not exist at the time of its composition.

When in 1961 I dedicated my book *African Genesis* to Marais' memory, I wrote:

> As no gallery of modern art can fail to be haunted by the burning eyes of Vincent Van Gogh, so the pages of no future science can fail to be haunted by the brooding, solitary, less definable presence of Eugène Marais.

At that time, we knew of the existence of the manuscript through his letters. And we knew its theme: *the evolutionary origins of the subconscious mind in man.* But after his death in 1936, the manuscript could not be found. And a quarter of a century later it seemed lost forever.

But then with the recovery of *The Soul of the Ape*, and its publication by Human and Rousseau Press (Johannesburg, 1969), Marais' presence in the sciences has taken on a more arresting definition. But it remains no less solitary, no less brooding; and no less, like some lost and recovered portrait itself, a tragic masterpiece.

*

Eugène Marais was born in South Africa in a farming community near Pretoria in 1871. In a letter he described it as "an isolated *uithoek*, as completely cut off from the rest of the civilised world, as the loneliest isle in the Pacific".

His family was Afrikaner, of the same people who in the 1830s had abandoned the Cape of Good Hope to the new domination of the English and had driven their ox-teams, their covered wagons, and their herds far north into the African interior to found their own republics, the Transvaal and the Orange Free State.

These people, in turn, were descendants of the original settlers sent out to the Cape by the Dutch East India Company in the later 1600s. Although we tend to think of the Afrikaner as entirely

The Marais homestead

Dutch-derived, in fact there were many French among them. Huguenots, they had taken refuge in Holland; and the Dutch government, not knowing quite what to do with them, sent off many along with their own colonists to that shining end of the world, the Cape of Good Hope.

Marais is a common name in South Africa. I have heard the joke made that had there not been among those early settlers two Frenchmen named Marais, both of enormously prolific potential, South African telephone directories would be many pages shorter. French though the name may have been to begin with, today it is as typically Afrikaner as 'Van der Merwe'. Within a very few generations after the founding of the colony in 1652, Dutch and French had merged their peoples into the identity we know as the Afrikaner, speaking the language we call Afrikaans.

The history of his people and their language, we shall see,

entered like some old, fated burden into the life of Eugène Marais.

There are contradictory versions of Marais' early life, even of his place of birth. His son, for example, believes his father to have been born in Pretoria, but I am drawing my version largely from Marais' own account (however unreliable) as described in letters to his translator in London, Dr Winifred de Kok, all written shortly before his death.

The letters have never been published, but each is a testament to his wit, his compassion, and his perception – not to mention his mastery of the English language. In one he writes:

> My first schoolmaster – in fact the only one procurable
> during my boyhood days – was a missionary of the
> Church of England, who is still alive and has risen to high
> honours in the hierarchy of his communion. He has
> never learned to speak a word of Afrikaans.

From the years of his earliest education Marais was acquiring his admiration on the one hand, and his resentment on the other, of all things English.

He seems to have spent some of his early years in Pretoria, some in the Orange Free State, and he finished his schooling in Paarl, the lovely vineyard-fenced town in the Cape. When he settled in Pretoria, the capital of the Transvaal Republic, he began the first of his careers, as a journalist.

Such was his energy that by 1890 he was editor of *Land en Volk*, and by 1892 when he was twenty-one, he owned it. His son reports that his father's comments as a parliamentary reporter were so caustic that he received the first of many honours: exclusion from the press gallery by resolution of the entire *Volksraad*.

Later, as a consequence of his resolute attacks on the mighty Paul Kruger, president of the Transvaal, he received a still higher honour: indictment for high treason. He was acquitted by the Pretoria Supreme Court.

It was during this period of journalism that he was introduced to morphine. He suffered severely from neuralgia, and the drug was easily available. In 1894, when he was only twenty-two, he married Aletta Beyers, only to see his young wife die the following year after the birth of their son.

How much this blow contributed to his later, lifelong addiction we cannot know. Quite shortly, he gave up his career in Pretoria and went to London, where on the advice of friends he studied law. He refers in his letters to medical studies as well, and his understanding of physiology would seem to confirm it. But by the time of his admission to the bar at London's Inner Temple, the Boer War had begun.

No episode in modern history so acted to give imperialism a bad name as Britain's war against the Boers. So long as the little republics of the Transvaal and the Orange Free State consisted of nothing but a few communities of outland farmers with a peculiar language and peculiarly independent ways, there was little to tempt the acquisitiveness of great powers. But when in 1886 gold was discovered on the reef where Johannesburg now stands, and there began a rush for the Witwatersrand to which not even the Klondike can be compared; then it could have been predicted with certainty that the peaceful years had ended. Britain launched its war of conquest in 1899, and in London, Marais became an enemy alien on parole.

With ease we forget our own past obscenities: with difficulty we forget the obscenities of others. We tend today to dismiss the Boer War as a tiresome episode in somebody else's history. But it was a war obscene in both purpose and execution.

Unable to inflict final defeat on the Afrikaner commandos and their guerilla tactics, Lord Kitchener turned to a scorched-earth policy and introduced to the language of the twentieth century the term 'concentration camp'.

The high *veld* was devastated, crops and farmhouses burned, livestock driven off, Boer families pressed into camps. It is true that over a hundred thousand survived the concentration camps. But it is also true that by the war's end, twice as many Boer wives, children, and elderly had died of Kitchener's new invention as Boer men had died before British guns. The Afrikaner would never forget.

And Eugène Marais never forgot. The private tragedy which morphine would bring to his life was now compounded by the public tragedy of his people. While according to his letters his intention had been to qualify in medicine as well as law, by the end of the war in 1902, he had escaped from Britain and was in Central Africa with an expedition trying to get munitions and medical supplies to his countrymen across the Limpopo.

He was too late. Decades later, in September 1935, writing to his translator in London, he recalled the circumstances of his education in English, of his long experience in London, and of the final defeat. And he wrote:

> You will perhaps be astonished to learn what my psychological 'reactions' were to the jumble of circumstances. The most enduring result was that it made me far more bitter than men who took part in the war at a more advanced age and who had had less to do with the English before the war.
>
> It was for purely sentimental reasons that I refused to write in any language but Afrikaans, notwithstanding the fact that I am far more fluent and more at ease in

English. I have written several monographs in other languages; but they were all scientific and most of them were at once consigned to the oblivion of archives of learned societies.

The nearest I ever attained to 'publication' in this connection was a monograph of mine included in the annals of the Smithsonian Institution, a thing which I believe is regarded as a desirable honour by scientists throughout the world.

Ours is the good fortune that he wrote his lost, unfinished masterpiece, *The Soul of the Ape*, in his own easy English. Eugène Marais Jr believes that his father intended it for the Smithsonian Institution in Washington. But it was Marais' tragic fortune that the pain of his people became so intensely his own that he confined almost all of his writing to a language understandable by so few. Not until after his death were translations of his two classics, *My Friends the Baboons* and *The Soul of the White Ant*, published in English.

There is a degree of disagreement as to the exact date when Marais initiated his studies of animals in a state of nature. In *African Genesis*, I wrote:

> ...so deep was his depression immediately following the war that, renouncing the society of men, he retreated to the Waterberg, a mountain fastness in the northern Transvaal, and accepted the society of animals. The date, one must calculate, was 1903.

The internal evidence of *The Soul of the Ape* roughly supports this calculation. As Marais describes the situation, his intimacy with the baboons of the Waterberg was only possible because for years the area had been depopulated; the animals had heard no gun fired, and it would still be some time before the ruined farmers and their families would return to resume their lives. We now know, however, that in Central Africa, Marais contracted malaria, an affliction which would recur throughout his life. In 1903 he was hospitalised in Portuguese East Africa, and not till the following year did he return to Pretoria.

We may never know the exact date when Marais retreated to the Waterberg. We can be sure only that it was at an early moment in the century, and that when he and a companion took up residence near a large wild troop of chacma baboons, he became the first man in the history of science to conduct a prolonged study of one of man's primate relatives in a state of nature.

But we must not overstate his then role as a scientist. He was a novice. No boy could have grown up as did he, of course, in the South African back country and fail to be fascinated with animals and their ways. Whatever medical training he may have had in London to forward his sophistication in the natural sciences, his legal training sharpened his sense of observation and proof.

But Marais was untrained and, in the field of animal observation, unsophisticated. In *The Soul of the Ape* he emphasises the handicaps of isolation – the lack of libraries, and the means of finding out what others had accomplished.

But wisely he adds:

> We approached this investigation without any
> preconceived ideas, and although at the beginning
> inexperience may have left much to be desired in our
> methods, we had at least no theories to verify.

Since Marais was scaling a scientific Matterhorn that no man had ever attempted before, it was well for him – and for us – that he carried no obsolete luggage. The early vignettes of his life in the Waterberg are the substance of the volume *My Friends the*

Baboons. They are among the most charming tales ever told by a naturalist. It would be almost sixty years before a comparable study of the wild baboon would be made by trained observers, and the wonder is not that this untrained pioneer should have made errors of observation and interpretation, but that his sight in general should have been so true.

Nevertheless, the reader seeking the facts rather than the joys of life should proceed with care. In his letters, Marais wrote:

> As a matter of fact, I have always been a little ashamed of these tales, they lie so far outside the sphere of what I have always regarded as my real work. They appeared as *feuilletons* in an Afrikaans newspaper and were never intended to assume a more enduring apparition.

The scientist who in his maturity would write *The Soul of the Ape* may well have been embarrassed by the early tales. But *My Friends the Baboons* has endured, despite its author's qualms, as a slim, unforgettable volume, the first of its kind in our literature. And the three years in the Waterberg not only relieved Marais for at least a time from the pain of a world from which he had fled, but immersed him in animal wonders that, taking shape in his mind, would provide the frontier for a new science.

Later in this essay I shall come back to the years in the Waterberg, since they furnish a main stage as well as major inspiration for *The Soul of the Ape*. His work there no longer possible, he returned to Pretoria to establish himself as an advocate and resume to an extent his career as a journalist.

Through the years, however, he seems never to have ceased his serious progress as a scientist, or to have lost contact with the bush and *veld*. His main preoccupation took form: the human psyche. With that preoccupation, his life work took two roads:

the study of those animals most like ourselves – the primates – and the study of those most unlike ourselves – the social insects. And as if all this were not enough, he began to find in his native language the materials of the poet.

Throughout its history the Afrikaans language had been largely of a vernacular sort. Then perhaps as another psychological consequence of the Boer War, a surge of literary activity came about. Given Marais' morbid dedication to Afrikaans, his fascination for the movement may easily be understood.

As early as 1885, when he was fourteen, he had written his first poem in English. But *Winternag* was one of the earliest of his Afrikaans poems to find high place in the new literature. In it, and in all his poetry, one finds a brooding, a melancholy, an expression of man's fate.

One of the most memorable is *Mabalel*, a haunting fable of the chieftain's lovely daughter who in all gay innocence ran down to the bank of the Limpopo for water:

> *Vinnig langs die paadjie trippel Mabalel*
> *Vrolik klink die liedjie*
> *Wat die klingelinge van haar enkelringe vergesel*

> Swiftly down the footpath comes tripping Mabalel
> And gaily sounds the song she sings
> To the rhythm of her tinkling ankle rings.

Nothing could warn her that in the depths waited the crocodile, Lalele. No word, no thought, no hint could penetrate the innocence to speak of a monster ever-waiting. Marais' lifelong burden of pain, of compassion, of perception, all combine in the single poem. And somehow, too, the poem speaks of that devouring secret side – despite all gaiety, despite all charm – like Lalele, lying, always waiting, in the depths of Marais' own nature.

A good many years ago Professor J. S. Weiner, Oxford's celebrated anatomist, told me a story about Marais that better than any other I have ever heard probed the hidden darkness.

Weiner is a South African who grew up in a district of Pretoria called Sunnyside and many years later achieved world fame when, with Kenneth P. Oakley of the British Museum, he proved that the Piltdown skull, then presumed to be the remains of man's earliest ancestor, was a hoax. I had never met Weiner when, in Rome for a conference, he came to our apartment to spend an evening. And he startled me, for he had no more than found a chair before he asked why I had dedicated *African Genesis* to Marais.

There was little to explain. I replied that I felt science had neglected Marais, and that, while I was not a scientist, it had seemed the least I could do.

"I'm glad you did it," said Weiner. "I know I've always felt guilty about him." And he told his story.

When Weiner was a boy in Sunnyside, one of the most thrilling of events was the sight of Eugène Marais – dignified, dressed always in immaculate white – walking down towards the river in the evening. It was a signal to all the children along the street. They came piling out of yards and gardens and upstairs rooms to follow Marais to the river. There he'd find an old stump or a log to sit on, while they arranged themselves on the ground. And he would tell stories.

All of his acquaintances recall him as one of the most consummate story-tellers of his time and place, but the mightiest of witnesses were the children at his feet, listening with held breath to his stories of bush and *veld* and dusty roads where mambas slink. The dark would come on. He would rise and go home, and the children, full of magic, would return to new worlds.

Marais had a room in a house just a few doors down the street. Weiner's sister, friendly with several girls who lived in the house, had come to know him, and one day asked Weiner to return a book to Marais' room. Clutching the book, consumed by the excited possibility of meeting the magic-maker alone, he went to the house, found the room, and knocked. There was no answer. He tried the door. It was unlocked. He entered cautiously. The room was dank with disorder. And there was a strange smell. He put down the book and fled.

Many years later – in 1940, years after Marais had died – Weiner was a medical student at St George's Hospital in London. In a pharmacological course the students were learning to identify a variety of pharmaceutical items. He was handed a sample of some drug with a very strange smell. Instantly he had a vivid recollection – a total recall – of a room somewhere. He struggled to identify the room, and knew it must be somewhere in South Africa. Then it came to him – it was Marais' room. And the drug was morphine.

Throughout Marais' life there were the long periods of intense study and outpourings of work when he was in command of his life at whatever inner cost. During such periods, he continued his observations of the termite and organised his revolutionary conclusions concerning the insect's social life. Also during such periods, he continued his observations of the baboon both in the wild and in captivity. He also planned and executed his experiments with the human subconscious and its hyper-sensitivity under hypnosis, and wrote (but did not quite finish) *The Soul of the Ape*.

And then there were the periods of breakdown, when friends

spoke delicately of his 'bad health'. But always, he regained command of himself, and returned to his work. And so it is reasonable to surmise, I believe, that the plagiarisation of his work by a world-famous European author was a major factor in his last collapse.

*

So far in this essay I have emphasised his work with baboons. Of equal importance, and at the farthest point removed on the animal spectrum, was his study of the termite, in his day called the 'white ant'. His scientific scheme was clearly defined: to investigate on the one hand the evolution of mind in that family of animals leading to man; and to study on the other hand the evolution of instinct in that branch leading to the most complex of insect societies.

And he came to a stunning conclusion.

Termitaries, as one sees them so frequently in Central and Southern Africa, are tall, compacted columns of earth sometimes twelve or fifteen feet high. Within lives the society, with its castes and its ranks, in countless number.

Marais concluded that all members of the colony and the termitary itself form what is essentially a single organism. The termitary itself is the body. The various castes in the society have the functions of the body's organs, with fungus gardens contributing the digestive tract, soldiers and workers acting as the cells of the blood stream, the queen the brain as well as the reproductive organs, and even the sexual flight executing the function of sperm and ova.

How they all communicate we do not know, but the 'soul' of the white ant – the *psyche*, we could say – is the property of the entire society.

Marais' conclusion was new and radical. Intending to gather all of his studies into a book one day, he began in 1923 to publish a series of articles in Afrikaans newspapers and the widely circulated magazine *Die Huisgenoot*. While Afrikaans is all but a secret language to the world at large, Dutch and Flemings read it without difficulty. And Maurice Maeterlinck was a Fleming.

A definitive article was published by *Die Huisgenoot* in 1925. Maeterlinck, dramatist and poet, was then a reigning figure in continental literature. Early in his career he had published *The Life of the Bee*, a mixture of philosophy and natural history, but he was not a scientist. Maeterlinck's reputation rested solidly on a long line of poetic dramas, and in 1911, shortly after the production of *The Bluebird*, he was awarded the Nobel Prize for literature.

How a man of such stature could in later years commit such a crime, I do not know. But in 1926, the year after the appearance of Marais' article, Maurice Maeterlinck published in French a book that by the following year appeared in English and in several other languages. In that book, and without acknowledgement, Maeterlinck took half of Marais' lifework and published it as his own. *The Life of the White Ant* stands even today on many a library shelf, but the name on its cover is that of a shameless plagiarist.

In South Africa there was a furore. When Dr de Kok in London in 1935 was beginning her translation of Marais' *The Soul of the White Ant*, he wrote to her, recalling the episode:

> You must understand that it was a theory which was not only new to science but which no man born of woman could have arrived at without a knowledge of all the facts on which it was based; and these Maeterlinck quite obviously did not possess. He even committed the *faux pas* of taking certain Latin scientific words invented by me to be current and generally accepted Latin terms.

The publishers in South Africa started crying to high heaven and endeavoured to induce me to take legal action in Europe, a step for which I possessed neither the means nor the inclination.

The press in South Africa, however, quite valorously waved the cudgels in my behalf. The *Johannesburg Star* (the biggest English-speaking daily in South Africa) published plagiarised portions which left nothing to the imagination of readers.

The Afrikaans publishers of the original articles communicated the facts to one of our ambassadorial representatives in Europe, and suggested that Maeterlinck be approached.

Whether or not this was done, I have never ascertained. In any case, Maeterlinck, like other great ones on Olympus, maintained a mighty and dignified silence.

That a Nobel Prize winner and a literary figure of such renown could have stolen half the life-work of an obscure South African genius must leave one bewildered. How could he have done it? Yet Maeterlinck's guilt is clear. With the admirable cooperation of the Johannesburg newspaper to which Marais referred, I have obtained from the 1927 file copies of the original report.

Marais' was a star-struck, star-crossed life; and with the Maeterlinck episode the stars, I suggest, crossed once too often. The crocodile Lalele always lay waiting within the dark pools of his being. Despite his objective, even humorous, recollections of the crisis in letters of later years, I do not believe that he ever regained the scientific urgency that had commanded his earlier investigations.

He wrote several popular summations of his work. He published several excerpts from *The Soul of the Ape*, rewritten into Afrikaans. But I find no record of scientific accomplishment after

1927. And we may recall that it was 1929 when young Weiner encountered the smell of morphine in Marais' room.

Morphine and misfortune beyond mortal endurance combined slowly, ever so slowly, to put out the light. It flared once more, however, undimmed and undaunted, in a letter to Dr de Kok written on 20 October 1935.

Earlier, he had written that after she finished the translation of his termite articles, they might consider what was to be done about his unfinished and unpublished *The Soul of the Ape*. "But," he confessed, "I write this in bed under the spur and inspiration of enduring pain," and spoke of his inability to find energy or enthusiasm for the work.

Now, however, he wrote the following:

> You see that your kindly enthusiasm has infected me! The thought of reaching a bigger public intrigues me. You must know that a great deal of the work I did and my interpretations of the results will be new to science. No other worker in the field ever had the opportunities I had of studying primates under perfectly natural conditions. In other countries you are lucky if you catch a glimpse of the same troop twice in a day. I lived among a troop of wild baboons, and for three years I followed them on their daily excursions; slept among them; fed them night and morning; I learned to know each one individually; taught them to trust and to love me – and also to hate me so vehemently that my life was several times in danger. So uncertain was their affection that I had always to go armed – with a Mauser automatic under my left armpit, like an American gangster!
>
> But I learned the innermost secrets of their lives. You will be surprised to learn of the dim and remote regions of the mind into which it led me. I think I discovered the real

location in nature of the hypnotic condition in the lower animals and men. I have an entirely new explanation of the so-called subconscious mind, and the reason for its survival in man. I think that I can prove that Freud's entire conception is based on a fabric of fallacy.

No man can ever attain to anywhere near a true conception of the subconscious in man who does not know the primates under natural conditions.

Please don't worry about the health business. It was silly of me to write in the strain – just a period of gloom to which I am occasionally subject. Accept my thanks and salutations.

Sincerely yours,
Eugène N. Marais

On the following 29 March, he killed himself.

*

Back in 1895, when Eugène Marais' wife lay dying, Sigmund Freud, working in Vienna, made one of the supreme discoveries of modern science. Using hypnosis as a tool, he discovered in patients suffering from hysteria the influence of unconscious forces on our psychic processes. The existence of these forces has never since been seriously disputed.

Beneath all our actions, our decisions and dreams, our regrets, our hopes, the little lies that we tell each other and the big lies that we tell ourselves, works an engine of which we are unconscious: it reinforces or distorts our conscious, seemingly rational minds.

The human psyche has frequently been compared to an iceberg. And in the early days of the polar flight from Copenhagen to California, when planes were smaller and still flew low enough and slow enough for the passenger to see something, there was a wonderful sight along the way.

Crossing the Denmark Strait between Iceland and Greenland, you looked down on icebergs floating south. Each was a white jewel glittering in the low northern sun, and were you a passenger viewing the icy mountain from a ship's deck, this would be all that you would see. But from one's window in heaven you saw far more. Painted turquoise by the waters, the immense underwater mass of the iceberg spread all about beneath your eyes. Majestic the frosty mountain of ice might be; but hidden in mighty mystery was the force that supported it. And such is the unconscious mind.

While I believe it true that the reality and the significance of Freud's discovery have never encountered other than superficial dispute, the same cannot be said of its nature. We have argued to this day as to just what the unconscious consists of. And if we are to set our compass as we approach Marais' venture into the unknown, then we must acquire a little perspective: we must see it as a part of one of our century's most profound scientific controversies.

To begin with, we should understand that *The Soul of the Ape* is a poet's title for a scientific work. It is symbolic. I suggested earlier that where Marais used the word 'soul', we should more prosaically say 'psyche'.

But beyond that, his reference to the ape may prove disconcerting for some. The principal object of his study was the baboon; not an ape at all, but an overgrown and extraordinarily intelligent monkey. The difference is immaterial. What Marais was observing was the evolution of mental processes in higher primates, and what he concluded from the baboon could only carry greater force in the more highly developed chimpanzee or gorilla.

A second point of early reassurance should be demanded; that concerning the authenticity of the document. We have, of course, the original manuscript in Marais' handwriting, and for anyone familiar with his work and thought, the question would probably not arise. Nonetheless, it must be admitted that we know very little, at least at present, about the manuscript's history. Letters to his son suggest that it was written in 1922, and friends of the period recall that at that time he talked of little else.

But what happened to it? We know that in 1935, writing to his translator, he referred first to his inability to finish the work, and then to his excitement concerning it. When some months later Dr de Kok received the news of his death, she immediately wrote to his son inquiring about the manuscript.

On 12 May 1936, Eugène Marais Jr replied:

> I also received your letter asking me for the field books
> and notes of my father. I am sorry, there are none. All
> that I got was about a third of a sack of papers – old
> letters, accounts, and your contract. There is no sign of a
> manuscript, and no notes.

Dr de Kok was unaware of the existence of the manuscript until I wrote to her in the spring of 1968, after receiving a copy myself from the Cape Town publishers. They in turn had been unaware of its existence a few months earlier, when they had invited me to write an introduction to a volume of Marais' minor pieces.

In the meantime, the manuscript was submitted to them by the son. Where had it been in the meantime, through all the years? Truly lost? Or hidden? And by whom, and why?

The mystery must remain a vexing question. But the reader has the right to ask; is it authentic? Is it possible that a document almost half a century old can today make a dynamic and original contribution to the evolutionary approach to human understanding, a scientific trend that has thrived only for the past few years?

By good fortune, we need not speculate. Solid evidence exists concerning the author and the approximate date of his work. In 1926, just before the ruin of the Maeterlinck episode, Marais published in English a paper called *Baboons, Hypnosis, and Insanity*, in a journal called *Psyche*, almost as obscure as himself. Several years ago my younger son excavated it in the library of Harvard University, and I have in my possession a photocopy.

In that article, Marais briefly summed up what one now recognises as the material and general conclusions of *The Soul of the Ape*.

He wrote:

> Inevitably the conviction gathers force that the so-called 'subliminal soul' – the subconscious mentality – is none other than the old animal mentality which has been put out of action by the new mentality.

It was the essence of his discovery. Had the book been published in its own day, so scanty was our then understanding of evolution that it would have been ignored. Today, it will still be disputed by the slower minds within our academic community, but just as there is little question about the manuscript's authenticity, there is also little question but that our sciences of human understanding are only now beginning to catch up with Marais.

And so a larger question than authenticity looms before us: How can it be that this solitary man, pursuing his lonely work amid tortured thoughts, could have been quite so far ahead of his time?

Or to turn the question around: how can it be that in the first seven decades of the century after Charles Darwin's, world science

32

INTRODUCTION

– the core of modern civilisation – is only now getting around to certain probable facts of life so apparent to Eugène Marais?

It is a story as remarkable as that of Marais himself, and, so far as the welfare of man is concerned, even more tragic.

*

Let us return to Freud.

The discovery of the role of the unconscious in the human psyche took place, as I have said, near the turn of the century. Sigmund Freud then pioneered the technique of psychoanalysis as a more practical substitute for hypnosis in exploring the hidden psychic channels of a disturbed patient, and bringing out into the area of consciousness the guilt and repressed memories which had contributed to the disturbance.

But the Viennese master became enamoured with the sexual impulse as the central force in the human unconscious. His preoccupation with sexuality brought him into furious conflict with the prim intellectual leftovers of the Victorian age.

It also brought him into conflict with his two most eminent colleagues and disciples.

Alfred Adler, unable to stomach the sexual monopoly, saw in the drive for power and dominance a more profound ingredient in the unconscious forces of our behaviour. Present research into animal behaviour may confirm Adler's position, and bring about a resurgence of his reputation.

Carl Jung turned from the overheated corridors of sex to the cooler rooms of myth and religion for fresh explanations.

But Freud continued to dominate the main stage of psychic investigation. To him, the sexual drives and frustrations of parents and children dominated the formative struggle for the adult unconscious mind. He gave us the Oedipus complex as a universal

33

attribute of man, inherited from primal days when within the confines of the family the sexual desire of the son for his mother encounters the implacable hostility of the father.

Freud's errors were many, and in his time perhaps unavoidable. He saw man's primal social unit as the family, as it unquestionably was not. He saw the sexual drive as dominating the actions of all higher animals, which just as unquestionably it does not. He lived and worked in a special corner of the bourgeois western world at a time when sexual repression was at its most severe; and from this passing, parochial base he extended timeless generalisations to all mankind. And besides all this, he worked exclusively with the sick, drawing from them improbable conclusions concerning the healthy.

We may be grateful to Freud that he presented us with the concept of the unconscious mind. And we may be grateful also that it was largely his sensational preoccupation that in the end would crush the sexual taboos of his time. Yet we may note in passing that today, when sexual repression is vanishing at such a startling pace, we see no comparable reduction of mental illness.

This was the 'fabric of fallacy' to which Marais referred in his letter to his translator. He did not live to witness the spread of a new fabric of fallacy which would challenge the old.

Sigmund Freud published *Beyond the Pleasure Principle* in 1920, two years before Marais wrote *The Soul of the Ape*. In this work Freud went beyond anything earlier and postulated the presence in all organisms, including man, of a life force which he called Eros, its most obvious manifestation being the sexual drive, and a death wish. We – man, snail, baboon, grizzly bear – come into this world with a will to live and a wish to die. When the wish overcomes the will, we have had it.

With this far-out excursion into metaphysics, Freud in time would shake off all but his most truly devoted adherents. And the concept of the death wish, impossible for any biologist to accept, may for all we know have opened the door for equally implausible concepts put forward by younger psychologists. But we should make the gravest of errors if we dismissed Freud's theory simply because it is preposterous.

From first to last throughout all his long career, Freud granted the force of instinct in the human psyche. With his newest theory he reasserted his belief in the unity of all living things, and he still saw man as a portion of the natural world. Then in 1924 the University of Chicago's John B. Watson published his *Behaviorism*. Watson believed in neither.

It is an accident of history that Marais recorded his thoughts concerning the human psyche at that moment, in 1922, when psychology's arrow was over the mid-Atlantic, halfway in its flight from Vienna to Chicago. It left behind a fractured, doubting, bitterly divided remnant of twentieth century psychology's pioneering band, to fall into the hands of a man who had not a doubt in a single bone of his head.

Psychology's pioneers had been human, sensitive, courageous, wild in their wonderings, magnificent in their frailties. They had been artists. Psychology's inheritor was a one-man advance agent for the computer age.

For the delicate intricacies of Viennese thought, Watson substituted a meat-hook, borrowed, we may assume, from a local South Side stockyard. His breath-taking confidence rivalled that of a Karl Marx issuing his *Manifesto*. Watson's most famous quotation runs as follows:

> Give me a dozen healthy infants, well-formed, and my
> own specified world to bring them up in, and I'll
> guarantee to take any one at random and train him to
> become any type of specialist I might select – doctor,
> lawyer, merchant-chief, yes, even beggar – man and thief,
> regardless of his talents, penchants, tendencies, abilities,
> vocations and race of his ancestors.

In other words, man is born a perfect cipher, bringing nothing into this world but malleability under the pressure of environment. He is invariant, and we need not concern ourselves with individual differences, since every human baby born has precisely the same potential as every other baby born. Talent, intelligence, capacity for leadership or the perfect crime – all are products of learning and experience within the lifetime of the individual. If as adults we vary, it is only because of the varying environmental experiences that have come our way, some adding to, some subtracting from, the uniform human potential.

This was Watson's behaviourism. He drew heavily on the work of the famous Russian physiologist Ivan Pavlov, who initiated systematic study of the conditioned reflex. Behaviourism was the perfect psychology for a materialist society.

There is an irony in our supposition that the United States and the Soviet Union live in worlds apart as well as opposed. Both of our societies are founded on materialism – the dialectic materialism of communism, the utopian materialism of capitalism. We must both believe in the omnipotence of the material environment. If the Soviets lose that faith, then they must cease to believe that the environment of a perfect socialist society will produce a new and perfect man. If we lose that faith, then the United States of America must cease to believe that in a society of perfect, universal affluence, all men will be good and true.

INTRODUCTION

The American dream and the Russian dream are of course constructed of nonsense, bearing minimum relation to human reality. And we may speculate that the dream has contributed its incisive share to the deepening and, seemingly insoluble, troubles which both super-powers are experiencing today. Most demonstrable is the fact that behaviourism – or environmentalism – dominates the political, philosophical, and scientific thought of America and the Soviet Union in equal measure, and more successfully than in any other countries in the contemporary world.

With very slight modifications in the direction of common sense, behaviourism in the United States passed from Watson at Chicago to Clark Hull at Yale, and to B. F. Skinner at Harvard. No figure in American psychology today rivals Skinner's authority. All over the American academic map, there are maverick scientists attacking the postulate of man the born goose-egg, man the uniform replaceable part, man the strangest being in all the animate world, containing no ingredients other than those that his environment has placed in him.

Yet the rule of the conditioned reflex remains unbroken. (Today we speak of 'reinforcement theory'.) One of the most influential of American anthropologists, Ashley Montagu, could recently write, without qualification, that

> ...man is man because he has no instincts, because
> everything he is and has become he has learned to be
> from other human beings.

It is a fairy-tale world that was born two years after the writing of *The Soul of the Ape*. It is a fabric of fallacy far more rigid, far more impenetrable, far more wishfully, sentimentally persuasive than the Freudian postulates that Marais deplored. It has become, indeed, a disease confined not at all to the laboratories and text-books of psychologists. Its dogma of human uniqueness and human omnipotence has spread at epidemic pace to infect, to a considerable or great degree, all the sciences of human understanding, and much of lay thought as well. If the educated world is in trouble, then the wonder is small indeed. This has been its education.

We have here, then, the broad answer to my original question: What has happened to the sciences in the first seven decades of the century after Darwin's?

The answer is as simple as it is brutal: we have lost our way. And so we may find also the answer to the question as to how a single man in his lonely work could have been quite so far ahead of his time. Marais did not lose his.

One glimpses few omens of fortune in Marais' obscure life. And yet luck came his way – once. When circumstances combined, just after the turn of the century, to place him in the neighbourhood of a huge troop of wild baboons, fortune cloaked him as it had no other man. Even the Boer War, otherwise a force that so darkened his life, brightened the fortune.

In farming country, baboons, because of their persistent looting of crops, are regarded as vermin, and a bounty is placed on their scalps. Nature has provided us with no more accomplished bandit, other than man himself.

One must assume that the war between man and baboon has prevailed since the first black farmers, a thousand or more years ago, invaded baboon country. The baboon, no simpleton, has come to the natural conclusion that man is a poor companion. But, as I have briefly suggested, when Marais arrived in the Waterberg, for four years his baboons had heard no gun fired. Farms had been burned, families taken off to concentration camps, and the farmers themselves had been with the Boer commandos.

While Marais continued his studies, the men slowly came drifting back from prison camps to restore their demolished farms. But they had been disarmed. Eventually, of course, they regained guns and ammunition. In the meantime, however, peace still prevailed between baboons and men.

In Marais' day, only the most peculiar of circumstances could have made his observations possible. As he himself suggests, the condition was not quite natural. His troop was larger than any studied recently in the limited areas of African game reserves, and its size was probably due to isolation and low mortality over so many years. The ruling oligarchy of dominant males was necessarily larger. Also, there was a higher ratio of males to females than is normal; it is the irrepressible male who suffers higher mortality at the hands of man.

I do not believe, however, that any of these slight aberrations affects his conclusions concerning the psyche of the baboon. His was the luck to have available before him, year after year, the repeated testaments of daily life in a higher primate. Freud, with lesser luck, had only theory.

Eugène Marais, the damned and the saved, with all his complexities of inner pain and overwhelming insight – so difficult to explain in terms of the conditioned reflex or human uniformity – could gain from long, direct experience materials for his basic conclusion that the human psyche, like the human body, has evolved from the world of lesser animals.

There was still another element of luck in Marais' isolation: his protection from the ups and downs of scientific thought. His faith in Darwin was undiluted. In all charity to Freud – and, indeed, to Watson, though I grant it grudgingly – it must be recorded that in their day, the theory of evolution was in bad shape.

From 1859, when *Origin of Species* was published, Darwin's theory remained dominant in all the natural sciences until nearly the turn of the century. But laboratory gremlins were eroding its validity. Natural selection did not seem to work in the fashion which Darwin had anticipated. Many rejected the theory entirely. Others turned to Lamarck and the inheritance of acquired characteristics. Marais himself was tempted by Lamarck, as letters to his son make evident, but the temptation had no influence on his own theories and does not enter into *The Soul of the Ape*.

It was a time, however, of biological trouble from which Marais was fairly well insulated. Not until 1930, when the work of an inspired trio of geneticists – Sir Ronald Fisher, John Haldane, and Sewall Wright – founded the new science of population genetics, was Darwin's natural selection placed on an inarguable basis. Today we speak of 'synthetic' evolution – as first synthesised by Sir Julian Huxley – or 'neo-Darwinism' to describe evolution as biologists now understand it.

The wheel came around, in other words, to the number which Marais had originally chosen. But it must be admitted that for those in the midst of the pressure of scientific fashion, evolution did not offer a firm structure with which to deny the validity of false hypotheses. (For those who still cling to them, society can offer little but the benevolence of an old scientists' home.)

But there was a far more practical lack than sound theory in the early decades of our century, and that was our total ignorance of the behaviour of higher animals in a state of nature.

Until 1961, when Sherwood Washburn and Irven DeVore published their paper *The Social Life of Baboons*, with a single exception science possessed no reliable information whatsoever concerning the life of our nearest evolutionary relative, the primate, in a natural state. The exception was the work of the great American psychologist Clarence Carpenter, who, some thirty years after Marais, entered a Panama rain forest to conduct a systematic study of the howling monkey. Through the 1930s he followed on with similar studies of the gibbon and the rhesus monkey. They were ignored, just as I am sure that Marais' study would have been ignored had it been published in its time.

Tides of fallacy were running too strong to be intercepted by a few rocky facts. We had not in this lengthy period entirely ignored animal behaviour, but we had confined our observations to captive or domesticated animals in laboratories and zoos.

One of the most ill-starred events of our scientific century took place in 1932 when Sir Solly Zuckerman – another South African removed to Britain – published his *Social Life of Apes and Monkeys*. The book was a thorough, convincing study of the behaviour of baboons.

But the baboons were in the London zoo. That they were obsessed with sex lent support to the Freudian hypothesis. That in Zuckerman's opinion this sexual obsession provided the basic motive for primate society – a motive so different from human society, in which the temptations of fornication are a socially disruptive force – lent support to the notion that 'people are different'; which in the coming years would be the bread and meat of a sociology and an anthropology ignoring any evolutionary influence on man.

Until 1960, the book stood as a keystone in the tightly constructed arch of contemporary fallacy.

Then in 1961 began the new attack of evolutionary thought and techniques on academic orthodoxy. That was the year

Washburn and DeVore published their study of baboons in the wild. Even their single study demonstrated that the behaviour of primates in captivity bears little relation to their behaviour in a natural setting. The former is a frustrated being; the latter a busy fellow with much to absorb his energies besides sex.

Then through the 1960s came a regiment of scientists observing all manner of primates in a state of nature. All confirmed the complexity of primate life recorded by Marais in 1922. All proved that sexual obsession in the primate is a myth. Zuckerman's book stands today totally discredited.

But social scientists beyond counting remain still uninfluenced even today by the revolution taking place in the natural sciences.

Biology's revolution began in an inconspicuous way in 1937, the year after Marais died. It was announced by a scientific paper called *The Companion in the Bird's World* by Konrad Lorenz, an Austrian scientist who for years had been observing a variety of birds and mammals at his home on a wild stretch of the Danube shore. It presented a series of highly original hypotheses concerning the relation of instinct to behaviour in animal life. And with that paper, the science that did not exist during Marais' lifetime came into being.

Konrad Lorenz is known today as the father of ethology, the rapidly exploding science concerned with the biology of behaviour. Carpenter's early studies indeed preceded Lorenz's, but it was the impact and continued activity of the Austrian naturalist that brought ethology into being. Closely allied with him in the early years was Nikolaas Tinbergen, who transferred his activities from the continent to Oxford, where he established a pioneering department of animal behaviour. In 1951 Tinbergen's *Study of Instinct* established ethology as a scientific discipline that could be ignored not even by its angriest opponents.

Such opponents existed in plenty. Although the earlier studies by the new ethologists confined themselves strictly to animals, the essential concern with evolution implied that sooner or later we should be involved with the behaviour of men. Still, however, the quarrels remained within the sciences, and not, indeed, until 1966, when by singular fortune the English translation of Konrad Lorenz's *On Aggression* and my own *The Territorial Imperative* appeared almost simultaneously, did the debates of the scientists reach out to a large, informed, and profoundly concerned public.

Are there truths about man which have been hidden from our eyes and shielded from the education of our children? Marais believed so. If Konrad Lorenz is the father of biology's new challenge, then Eugène Marais was its prophet. But before we turn our attention to his book lying before us, we must inspect one relevant scientific development which Marais did not and could not anticipate.

*

It is a final irony in his story – and the story of our times – that in 1922, when he was writing *The Soul of the Ape* in Pretoria, a young Australian anatomist named Raymond Dart was arriving at the medical school in Johannesburg, only thirty-odd miles away. And two years later, Dart discovered *Australopithecus africanus*.

Any understanding of the evolutionary nature of man must rest on two sources of information: Firstly, we must know the world of the animal, gaining insight from it with which to view our own; in this Marais pioneered.

But also, we must know as precisely as possible the evolutionary course by which, from the condition of the lower animals, there arose that most remarkable of animals, man. This

Dart pioneered. But whereas Marais' work remained unknown, Dart's became the focus of a controversy which is being resolved only in the present day.

The problem of human evolution may be stated simply. When Raymond Dart discovered the fossil remains of a being who lived on the African savannah over a million years ago, who was a hunter following a carnivorous, predatory way of life, and who resembled man in every way except in brain size (about a third that of ours), he upset almost every preconception – philosophical, religious, biological – concerning what the human ancestor should be like.

Since the time of Darwin, we had assumed that our primal ancestors must have resembled the shy, inoffensive, vegetarian ape of the forest. I know of only one thinker, the British psychologist Carveth Read, who departed from that universal assumption. In 1920, he published his conclusion that our pre-human ancestor should be called *Lycopithecus*, for his way of life must have been similar to that of the wolf. Nobody paid any attention to Read.

Then four years later, Dart found the creature.

We speak of such predecessors as hominids, a primate line evolving independently of the lines of the ape and the monkey. When Dart claimed that his *australopithecines* were true hominids, that we lived in bands systematically and effectively killing for a living, and that we used tools and weapons long before the development of the enlarged human brain, it all combined to produce a bad case of scientific indigestion.

Today, at last, his case is all but closed. In late 1967 Alfred Romer, the world's foremost palaeontologist, wrote:

> With one or two exceptions, all competent investigators
> in this field now agree that the *australopithecines* of the
> early Pleistocene are actual human ancestors.

The question before us today concerns not the legitimacy of our carnivorous ancestry, but its antiquity. And it is the work of that Christopher Columbus of human evolution, Kenya's Louis Leakey, that we shall probably find the answer.

The 1960s, which have witnessed the explosion of discoveries in the area of animal behaviour, have witnessed a simultaneous explosion in our knowledge of the human past. I shall not detail the rapid advance, but merely describe the most recent of discoveries, announced only a few weeks before the writing of these pages.

In May 1968, Leakey delivered a shock that will probably once again put science into a state of trauma. At a site near Fort Ternan, in East Africa, he had been studying a creature which Leakey calls *Kenyapitchecus*, and who was probably ancestor of the *australopithecines*. There, in the midst of a fossilised bone pile to rival those of their descendants, Leakey has found stones used to smash up antelope bones in order to extract the marrow.

By modern techniques of radiogenic dating, the time may be reliably fixed at between twelve and fourteen million years ago. Dart's *australopithecines* were but yesterday.

The antiquity of the hominid hunting way – aside from all its implications in terms of human behaviour – separates our evolutionary track from that of the vegetarian ape or monkey through a span of time quite beyond our powers of imagination.

And so in reading *The Soul of the Ape* we must avoid at all costs the easy pitfall of equating the amiable nature of the chimpanzee – or, indeed, the aggressive behaviour of the baboon – with facets of human behaviour. We are all the end-products of quite varying evolutionary paths, and equally varying conditions of survival. But we are of the same primate family. And – all-importantly – we are all of us products of the same evolutionary process.

Eugène Marais could not know what the science of the future would reveal concerning the distinctiveness of human evolution, mediated by that long-surviving hominid, the wolf-ape. Dart's early discovery was too lost in controversy, and too late in Marais' declining life, to have influenced the course of his thought.

It is our good fortune, as well as his, that his concern with psychic evolution was so profound as to be applicable to us all – the harmless ape, the belligerent baboon, and killer man.

*

His was the first human mind to penetrate the secrets of the wonderful world of the animal, and to apprehend the legitimate mysteries of the wonderful world of man.

I wrote these words in *African Genesis*, and have now neither reason to modify them nor inspiration to improve them. Marais was not the first thinker to see in Darwin's theory implications concerning the continuity of our evolution in factors other than body.

In *Les Sociétés Animales*, Alfred Espinas attempted to demonstrate the gradual transition from animal to human societies, but his ideas were dismissed to oblivion by the master sociologist Emile Durkheim.

Carveth Read, as we have seen, took a hard look at the history of human ferocity and forecast with accuracy the wolf-like nature of the human ancestor.

None before Marais, however, had the living materials of nature to guide him. And none before Marais had the audacity to peer into the inner recesses of the primate mind, and to draw from his observations conclusions concerning the continuity of evolution of the human mind itself.

The bewilderment of man is the bewilderment of all higher primates. Mind was the essential blessing bestowed by an accident of mutation on the earliest of Eocene primates perhaps sixty million years ago.

We differed, otherwise, little from rodents. But since at this date we were all of us arboreal, we developed hands instead of paws, with fingernails to protect sensitive finger-pads so valuable to a life in the trees. And we had the social inclination; not since the most primitive of lemurs do we find a primate species of solitary disposition.

But the brain was our hall-mark. If the primate was to succeed as a natural experiment, then he must succeed by his wits.

Thus by whatever evolutionary track we proceeded – the ape and most monkeys in their forest setting living off forest foods; the baboon and a few other terrestrial monkeys, like the patas and the vervet, living an all-fours life largely in the open and eating a far greater variety of foods; or the advancing hominid with his bipedal posture, his hands freed for the use of weapons and tools, his diet more and more dependent on the fruit of his kill – in all of them, we find the pressure of natural selection favouring the better brain, and the better use of what brains we had.

The psychic dilemmas of the hominid and baboon – both of us citizens of the dangerous savannah – can with little likelihood have included qualitative differences. We both in our most ancient origins had been largely guided by the confidence of instinct.

Learning, we must recognise, plays a part in all animal life: the amoeba can 'learn'. Such learning, however, for the most part reinforces instinct and adapts its inherited directives to circumstances of time and place; it is still *instinct* that guides.

But in the progressive primate, and in many predators as well, such ancient wisdom fixed in the genes was not quite good enough. And so there developed the conflict, as Marais saw it, between the 'old' mind – the inherited animal mind – and the 'new' mind, which is developed in the individual by experience.

The new mind would make possible the human achievement of adaptation to almost every environmental condition the earth has to offer. If genetic wisdom could offer us no information as to how to meet some new state of affairs, then experience and learning would succeed.

But, as Marais sets forth, the baboon, like man, has so succeeded. He has accepted all manner of climates, of conditions of survival, of enemies, of existence on lush plains or forbidding deserts, in mountain fastness or tempting valley. Like man, the baboon thrives on anything that passes for food.

Marais knew of baboons that killed lambs to gain the milk curd from their stomachs. He knew of none that ate meat.

But in recent years we have found areas in East Africa where baboons have crossed the rubicon that the hominid once crossed, and prey systematically on the gazelles' newborn fawns.

The baboon has faced everything, including the implacable animosity of man. Yet he survives as the second most successful of primates, surpassed only by ourselves.

I suspect that it was Marais' attention to traditions of behaviour varying from troop to troop that presented him with his first hard evidence for the significance of the new mind in baboon life. This forms a major scientific contribution in *The Soul of the Ape*. Even in studies of most recent years, we have been far too preoccupied with forms of behaviour which are common to an entire species – what we call 'species-specific' – and therefore probably under genetic control.

That we find in man such varying traditions of behaviour in different peoples has been a principal argument on the part of those who see the human species as differing radically from subhuman animals. Marais nullifies the argument with his careful documentation of varying traditions in baboon life.

A chief function of any society, human or subhuman, is education. Sir Arthur Keith once described education as the first industry of any species; should the industry fail, the species will become extinct.

Few higher primates centre their social life on the family. And so, with their slow-growing young, education is mostly accomplished through the traditions of the entire troop. The young learn from their elders what the elders when young learned from theirs; and so, whatever the wisdom gained from experience the troop may possess, it is handed down from generation to generation.

Man has the immense advantage of the oral or written word, but the process is the same.

I cannot believe that Marais would have been surprised that Japanese scientists, in their superb studies of the Japanese monkey, have found among ten troops three in which high-ranking adult males invariably take charge of all year-old infants when mothers give birth to new babies; three in which the tradition is sporadic; and four in which it never occurs at all.

In terms of the natural selection of groups, the first three troops have developed a tradition which through reduction of infant mortality is of superior survival value. And a thousand years from now, if there is still a Japan with Japanese monkeys, what is today a social invention may have become a tradition common to the species.

Obsolete information, cluttering the minds of those who speak for human uniqueness, still tends to inform us that there is a sharp line between animal and man because the animal is guided by rigid instinct, while man is guided by flexible rational powers.

Both propositions are false.

Our developing knowledge of human evolution must tell us that so gradual was our coming, no clear moment could ever have occurred when before it we were animals and after it, men. And any honest appraisal of the human being – any ruthless inspection of one's own inner self – must inform us that we are guided again and again by impulses lying deeper and more powerful than our rational determinations.

Man has his instincts. And so it was that Marais exposed the other side of the psychic coin: the baboon, a primate of quite undistinguished brain as compared with the chimpanzee, must still gain most of his directives for living from his power to learn.

Human Aggression, a recent book by the London psychoanalyst Anthony Storr, presents better than any other published thus far the evidence for man's hidden animal nature. And *The Soul of the Ape*, though written so long ago, presents better than any book published thus far the dawning humanity in the psyche of the higher primate.

One cannot be so innocent as to presume that the two books together will forever remove the mythical line between animal and man; but one may modestly hope to see some damage done.

*

Marais' observation of the role of learning and tradition and consequent varying behaviour in the life of the baboon is thus a major advance in our new evolutionary literature. His central contribution, however, is of course the book's central hypothesis: the evolutionary origins of the unconscious in man's mind. For this contribution we have little precedent.

If one has groped through the existing scientific literature devoted to instinct and learning, then one must grasp with relief at Marais' invention of two simple phrases, *phyletic memory* and *causal memory*.

By this I do not imply that they can be swallowed without a bit of chewing.

But 'phyletic' is not too difficult a word. In biology we refer to phylogeny when we speak of the history of a species and its antecedent species, as we speak of ontogeny to describe the history of the individual. A phyletic memory, then, is one whose cause we are unaware of, since the memory itself is carried in our genetic make-up as a result of evolutionary crises long ages past.

Let us think, for example, of some ancestral baboon species recently emerged from the life of the forest. Apes and arboreal monkeys have, as a rule, loose social organisations. But on the savannah the baboon met lethal dangers rare in the forest. Even the small-brained hominid himself, to judge by the fossil remains of his kitchen-middens, had a hearty appetite for baboon flesh. Now, the baboon is a powerful animal, but even so his only defence on the savannah lay in concerted social action. Those troops that kept to their undisciplined ways met disaster. Only those capable of leadership, willingness to obey, and cooperative defence could survive to leave descendants.

The hamadryas is an aberrant baboon species with its own

desert ways. But in all other species, throughout the passing millennia, the basic baboon society took form. There is a group of powerful males who never quarrel, who enforce order in the troop, and who assume the most dangerous responsibilities in the troop's defence. And there are all the other members who submit to authority and do their part. The leaders may be three in a troop of eighty and could be overwhelmed by revolution tomorrow. But it will not happen. Phyletic memory inhibits the impulses of the many with its genetic wisdom derived from ancient happenings, just as it commands the actions of the few to go forth at all risk, and face the cheetah.

Phyletic memory forms the unconscious portion of the baboon psyche. Causal memory is the conscious portion, the learned portion, the portion springing from experiences within the baboon's lifetime. As Marais saw them, the two exist side by side, or, more accurately, the old beneath the new. And the story of psychic evolution has been the gradual ascendancy of causal memory over the phyletic. Yet never does the one wholly succeed in displacing the other.

Turning to Marais' investigations of the phyletic memory in man, the startled reader may be wary of conclusions drawn from hypnosis. But we must recall that Freud too used hypnosis as a technique in his discovery of the unconscious mind.

Sir Julian Huxley, in *Essays of a Humanist*, writes:

> One of the darker chapters in the history of science and medicine is the way in which pioneer hypnotists were attacked and often hounded out of the medical profession. Even today, there is still a great deal to be discovered in this strange and exciting subject.

Just how strange it may be is illustrated by an experiment at Pennsylvania State University reported as recently as 1968. A group of college students were hypnotised and told that they were nine years old. Each was then instructed to write a letter to a friend. The letters were then mixed with similar letters written by actual nine-year-old children, and all were presented to a faculty committee who knew nothing of the experiment.

The letters by the hypnotised college students and those of the real nine-year-olds could not be distinguished on any basis – whether style, content, or handwriting.

Contemporary theories of learning tumble in the face of such an experiment; and it is not impossible that hypnosis was placed beyond the scientific pale because it asked more questions than our sciences could answer. A similar fate befell research into extrasensory perception.

But in Marais' day hypnotism was still regarded as a valuable and legitimate tool. If in our day it is very nearly taboo, then we may comfort our suspicions by reflecting that, strange though hypnotism may be, the ways of science can be stranger.

Phyletic memory is Marais' term for what we would call 'instinct'. Yet the word instinct is so loose, so difficult to explain or define, so surrounded by controversy, and so subject to manipulation by those who would justify the worst or the best in human behaviour as instinctive, that many authorities refuse to use it.

Marais, it seems to me, has provided us with a superior term for a quality in life which, if we cannot explain, we still cannot deny. With his *phyletic memory* and his *causal memory*, he described two psychic forces cleanly and with sufficient definition to permit his investigation of the evolutionary origins of the conscious and unconscious minds.

Marais, as I have indicated, saw phyletic and causal memory as existing apart, with the latter increasingly dominant over the former. They may, however, combine. Ethology is aware today of many forms of behaviour which, while having a genetic basis, require learning to become activated.

Such is the behaviour of a robin defending his acre, or a man defending his home. Both have ancient phyletic memories that possession of an exclusive territory forwards the survival of adult and offspring. But causal memory must help robin or man in gaining a territory, knowing its boundaries, its resources, and the character of potential intruders, or the pattern of behaviour will be incomplete.

Causal and phyletic memory may form an alliance in another fashion, and perhaps it might be useful in our own thinking to retain a distinction between the *unconscious* and the *subconscious*.

The truly phyletic memory would then be the true unconscious, something beyond any recollection, since its causes lie buried perhaps tens of millions of years before the birth of the individual.

But in deference to the psychologists of Freud's generation as well as to our own commonplace experience and observation, we must recognise the existence of a murky half-world, the subconscious. Here repressed causal memories sink, to join with rising phyletic memories to form powerful unions distorting or vetoing the rational procedures of the causal mind.

But there is a difference from the true unconscious. These unremembered memories, being causal, have their sources in the lifetime of the individual. And so, whether by psychoanalysis or other tools, they may be probed and, if we are lucky, brought back into the realm of rational disposition.

Let us take an example: Konrad Lorenz has demonstrated that no organism lacking aggressiveness has the probability of living to maturity and reproducing itself. Anthony Storr has applied the Lorenz principle to human life.

We may therefore regard aggression as one of the most powerful of phyletic memories.

But aggression in human life may take many forms, from the painting of masterpieces to competing in business to the killing of strangers.

Now let us assume that we live in a society that praises selflessness, condemns aggressiveness, provides few outlets for its healthy display, and instils in us a sense of guilt concerning temptations and experiences which are in themselves quite normal.

May not such causal memories – perhaps of the excitement of violent action acquired in early childhood – be forced by guilt into our subconscious, there to form union with phyletic command and to lurk in our depths, like Lalele?

Might not such a social attitude, judged in the terms of a future psychology, accomplish the precise opposite of its objectives?

There are few areas of human life, few moments of human decision, to which *The Soul of the Ape* does not bring a measure of clarification. I have said that the bewilderment of man is the bewilderment of the animal; and I firmly believe it is so.

We are caught, all of us, at our differing levels of psychic evolution between the opportunities of the new mind and the commands of the old. And perhaps in the end it will be recorded that we were all tragic species playing out the successive charades of a natural experiment called 'the primate', in which the last terrible writing on the wall was inscribed by the dainty hand of some forgotten lemur in the long-lost Eocene.

It need not, however, be true.

Man today has reached a bewilderment that no ape, no monkey could envy.

But we have something that, so far as we know, they have not: self-awareness. We have the power to investigate ourselves. And however foolishly we may use that power, denying by our folly even our rationality, still the power exists.

The evolutionist, looking wryly about at a world that sweet reason has produced, may well conclude that the efforts of the individual must in the end prove futile: that man makes no sense.

Yet while he could be right, he would also be wrong. Man may make no sense, but evolution does. And if through our self-awareness we can come to an understanding of ourselves and our place in nature, then through a simple faith in something far larger than ourselves we may find a hope which we so singularly lack today.

Perhaps a sense of individual futility was too strong in Eugène Marais. Perhaps causal memories of misfortune made union in his own subconscious with the phyletic memory of the monster Lalele. Perhaps his tragic sense as a poet overcame the creative optimism of the scientist. Perhaps he was a man born too soon, and knew it.

Or perhaps it was nothing at all so large, so profound, but that in an hour of inspiration he returned to his labours on *The Soul of the Ape* and found, as the weary months slogged by, that he was not too soon, but too late. And so he blew himself to pieces with a shotgun on a farm near Pretoria.

We shall never know.

Nor does it matter that much. His manuscript is rough. It lacks a proper conclusion. In certain areas of his argument, one longs for further demonstrations, and for those more detailed

An ex libris plate from a book owned by Marais

observations which he could undoubtedly have supplied.

Had Marais, in the southern autumn of 1936, been able to finish his manuscript, polish the rough parts, to rethink a few conclusions, add further ideas that had come to him in recent years, then beyond all question, he would have left us more than we shall find in the following pages.

But he left us enough. He gave us certain imperishable thoughts still new and useful in a time of human crisis. And he gave us something else: the memory of his own life, in itself an imperishable testament to the awesome wonders and the legitimate mysteries of the being called man.

THE SOUL OF THE APE

1
Means and Methods of Research

SHORTLY AFTER THE WAR, I had the opportunity of living for three years in very close proximity to a troop of wild chacma baboons (*Papio ursinus ursinus*). During that time a register was made of all the adults – or nearly all – and it was thus possible to study their behaviour under very favourable conditions. During most of this time I had the invaluable assistance of a young friend and countryman who, under the most disadvantageous circumstances, had attained a remarkable knowledge of the higher African mammals and their comparative anatomy. An untimely death unfortunately cut short his work.

The conditions under which this investigation was made were, in some respects, ideal and are hardly likely to recur in South Africa.

We were living in a high, narrow valley between two parallel ranges of the central mountains of the Waterberg in the Transvaal: a stream flowed down one side of this valley and found an outlet through a gorge in the southern range. The floor was strewn with piled-up fragments of conglomerate rock which, in the course of ages, had been dislodged from the hills to shape the faces of the precipitous walls of the gorge. Both floor and walls were thickly overgrown by big timber-trees and tree-ferns. Plants grew and thrived wherever the smallest root-hold had been gained either in the soil or in the living rock. Along this gorge the stream had worn for itself a very much impeded channel to the low country.

On the right side, about a hundred feet from the floor of the gorge, the face of the cliff was split by a huge level-floor cavity.

Just below this cave, against the wall of the precipice, grew a giant wild fig tree, its roots widespread over the face of the rock and its enormous branches and dense foliage completely sheltering the mouth. A slope of loose rock, which was comparatively easy to climb, stretched down from one end of the cave entrance to the floor of the gorge.

The cavity formed the sleeping place of a troop of baboons. The circumstances which rendered these clever and extremely nervous animals indifferent to the presence of their arch-foe, man, were due to a long succession of events.

The Boer War had left the area in unpeopled solitude for a number of years and, when eventually the families returned, the men were for several more years without rifles or ammunition. The baboons were very quick to realise the helplessness of their neighbours, and they took full advantage of it. The orchards, gardens and grain lands were raided with incredible fearlessness.

On our arrival in the valley and during the construction of our huts near the entrance to the gorge, the babies who could walk and all the youngsters of the troop showed an insatiable and often reckless curiosity, much to the alarm and disapproval of their elders. Perched on stones within thirty yards of us, they would follow with the closest attention all our movements.

These quiet times occasionally gave place to rollicking games, one of which was to approach us in a rush up to the sticking point of their courage, and from that comparatively safe distance they would indulge in the customary baboon face-pulling and threatening grimaces, or else assume an attitude of conciliation. (This attitude is referred to at length in the chapter dealing with sexual abnormality.)

The older individuals were at first very wary of approaching us. They would remain on the slopes of the hillside, nervously calling to and 'warning' the more intrepid youngsters, and occasionally a big male would wake the echoes of the mountains with his tremendous voice.

We experienced a great deal of difficulty in overcoming this distrust among the adults. It was my colleague who by infinite tact and patience eventually gained their confidence to such an extent that they assembled daily for several months in the immediate vicinity of the huts, where they were fed on 'mealies'. We were thus able, in time, to approach within a few yards of them, and it was then apparent that it was we, rather than the chacmas, who needed to be distrustful and continually on guard. We were never actually attacked, although dangerous threats were a daily occurrence, and of such a nature that in the beginning one of us had always to be armed.

But a better understanding was gradually established as we got to know each other. Eventually the baboons allowed us to climb up the slope of their sleeping place in the evening and very early morning, and watch them from the roots and branches of the big fig tree.

They would never, however, permit us to set foot on the floor of the cave itself. Any such attempt was at once, even in the night, countered by a threatening advance on the part of the big males, who clearly 'meant business'.

We kept a number of tame adults and babies, some in captivity and some at liberty, at a farmhouse below the mountains. We also had in captivity at different times wild adults that had been wounded by scalp-hunters (The Transvaal Government paid a bounty of 5s on every baboon scalp) and captured alive.

The behaviour of these captive baboons was studied for a

period not exceeding three years.

Ideal as conditions were in one respect, we still laboured under disadvantages that were not without effect on our work. The greatest of these was – it appeared later – the want of time.

As the neighbouring farmers regained possession of rifles and ammunition, observation of the troop became more and more difficult and all too soon was rendered quite impossible.

Another serious disadvantage was our isolation: we had no libraries, and no means of checking what work had already been accomplished in this field.

In this connection I would like to mention our own attitude towards the exploration of these twilight souls. We approached this investigation without any preconceived ideas, and although at the beginning inexperience may have left much to be desired in our methods, we had at least no theories to verify.

We tried always to adhere to the empirical method, and to avoid as far as possible the shadowy by-ways of metaphysical speculation and psychological abstraction to which research in this field seems inherently inclined.

We also decided against setting ourselves an exclusively anthropomorphic criterion; but this proved to be more attractive as a theoretical basis of research than efficient as a practical means of avoiding error.

It is true that a continual reference to human mentality is not the ready highway to truth that it seems to be at the first glance. There are profound – and, to the believer in the theory of continuous mental evolution, even startling – differences in the lesser eddies of the psychic stream. The great current is beyond doubt the same in kind, however much it may differ in volume and intensity, but it is in these lesser eddies that the significance becomes obscured by a continual reference to human psychology. This we realised clearly.

On the other hand, these differences excepted, the mental processes of the chacmas are generally so human-like that it proved impossible to submit them to a critical examination without accepting as a standard our common human experience.

It is necessary to state that the environment of this wild troop cannot be described as quite natural. They were completely isolated and had evidently been so for many years; the intrusion of man as a dominating element added other profound effects to those of unnatural isolation.

In a systematic study of behaviour these particular conditions would have been an advantage had it been possible to compare the habits of the chacma we investigated with those living under more natural circumstances.

But there were two great difficulties preventing such a comparison. The first was the problem of finding any troop where the reaction to man's intrusion had not created habits that would not have existed in his absence, and the second was the supreme difficulty of observing closely and continuously any troop not so circumstanced.

We did, however, observe some other wild troops under more natural conditions, as will be apparent in this record of a small portion of our work, which is basically an attempt to interpret some of the actions we studied in our troop compared with others less isolated, rather than a detailed description of the chacma's behaviour.

2

Habits Acquired in
Different Environments

AN OUTSTANDING CHARACTERISTIC of the chacmas is their ability to thrive in the most varied environments. They are equally at home on the fertile mountains of the Cape and in the sterile hills of our more northerly terrain. In the Cape they are in the midst of a plentiful and varying food supply. Here, as Darwin has pointed out, the proportion of different species of plants to the extent of soil area covered is greater than in any other continent, and no less plentiful and varied is the insect life.

The mountain masses of the Cape afford, therefore, a safe retreat in the midst of thickly populated districts, and their protective value is chiefly due to the fact that natural fertility renders it unnecessary for the baboons to engage in the dangerous expedient of exacting contributions from the farms of their human neighbours.

It is hard to imagine an environment more different from this land of plenty, with regular rains, sheltering caves, precipices and forests and perennial mountain streams, than the rugged, sterile hills of the north, where existence has become an unending struggle for the chacma.

Not only is his life more instantly jeopardised on these low and shelterless hills by the presence of man, but the question of a sufficient food supply has become a complex problem. Yet even here the chacma thrives under conditions which would, I should imagine, have brought about the extermination of any other species of gregarious mammal. Indeed, many great species of mammals have been exterminated in this country under conditions far more naturally favourable.

But there is an even more profound difference in natural environment than the one created by difference of locality only.

It is beyond doubt that the great majority of the species have only in recent times ceased to be arboreal animals and have migrated to the hills and mountains under pressure of defensive necessity and have become purely mountain animals. There are instances where such migrations have taken place within the memory of man.

But this change in natural habitat has not been universal. Along the great river-ways of South Africa in the less populated regions, there are still great numbers of baboons inhabiting the forests, where they live as largely arboreal animals.

It will be realised how very different their habits and general way of life must be to render existence possible under two such radically different sets of natural conditions. The 'tree' or 'river' baboon is popularly spoken of as a distinct variety of species, a designation which has no other foundation than these greatly divergent habits.

These different habits are not determined only by the difference in the natural food supply or by the difference in environmental dangers; they are brought about by conditions which affect the entire existence of the animal in its relation to nature.

They differ no less profoundly in some of their habits than, for instance, the klipspringer (*Oreotiagus saltator*) and the steenbok (*Neotraginus*). Nonetheless, they are the same species, and there is no morphological reason for describing the river baboon as a 'local variety' in the generally understood sense. Nor is there any hereditary limitation to one environment, as there would be in all lower animals similarly placed.

We established experimentally that if an infant arboreal baboon is given to a mountain troop, it is adopted and grows up with the complete knowledge necessary for it to exist in its new environment. (The reverse was not proved.)

Among the higher vertebrates the nature of their food supply is certainly a great element in determining the course of psychic and morphological specialisation: the aardvark (*Orycteropus afer afer*) – an animate digging machine, toothless, with its long sticky tongue, its wonderful instinct for locating deep termite nests in hard soil; the remarkable bodily structure of the giraffe; the conversion of the flying wings of the penguin into paddles – all were modifications selected primarily by the adoption of a special food supply, and this is the case in most higher animals.

It seems also to be a general rule in nature that any sudden change of environment involving the loss of natural food supply – although food for which the organism has not been specialised may be plentiful in the new environment – means destruction.

For instance, the South African otter can, in captivity, subsist on warm-blooded terrestrial animals exclusively, without ever entering water, and yet several instances came to our notice where otters were driven by drought to take up their residence at shallow inland pools without fish or crabs, and they invariably died of hunger, although small terrestrial animals abounded in these drinking places. It is hardly conceivable that structural modification in this case rendered the capture of sufficient animals to sustain life impossible. It was 'instinct' that stood in the way.

This example emphasises the fact that the psychic specialisation is generally more powerful in confirming an animal's reaction to a definite environment than correlated somatic modifications. It is true that species outside the order of primates have been known to adopt new habits because of radical change of food, but all the instances I know of clearly resulted from certain definite influences that are not present in the chacma.

In this country the rhinoceros-bird, which used to relieve the now vanished thick-skinned game of ticks, has undertaken the same office for the thinner-skinned domestic animals.

The removal of a tick from cattle frequently leaves a small open wound, and in such cases the bird eats the exposed flesh, often causing severe, if not fatal, injuries. From this habit it was an easy transition to the practice of attacking any open wounds on cattle. The Australian parrot which has taken to picking holes in the backs of sheep is similar. It is said the habit originated in a resemblance between the wool of the sheep and the covering of a fruit commonly eaten by the bird.

In these few instances, one principle invariably underlies the change of habit: the suggestive influence on the hereditary instinct directly conveyed by a natural food. In the chacma no such connection can be traced in the majority of new food habits.

The natural food of the chacma consists of fruits and insects. I know of no verified instance where, under natural conditions, the flesh of warm-blooded animals is habitually eaten.[1] Now if any two extremes of locality inhabited by the chacma are considered, it will be found that the species of insects and fruits which constitute their principal food supply vary greatly and, although the nature of the supply is identical, the means of utilising it differ more profoundly than in any other lower animals, however widely dispersed.

---

[1] In captivity they easily acquire the habit of eating cooked meat, as also they frequently acquire an inordinate craving for tobacco and alcohol.

But, in addition to these varying methods of procuring natural food, what may be described as supplementary habits have been acquired in different localities which are altogether outside the order of nature – as one conceives that order to exist in the case of the higher mammals – habits which at once place the chacma in a class by itself.

It is necessary to refer to only a few of these personally verified habits in order to convey an idea of the singularity of the animal in this respect.

The southern limit of the baobab tree (*Adansonia digitata*) is the far north of the Transvaal, where it grows to a great height and size, dominating the entire forest. It bears a fruit containing a sub-acid pulp popularly valued as a febrifuge and for making cooling drinks. This fruit is doubly protected, for it grows at such great height from the ground that until it drops, only birds and arboreal animals can reach it, and its outer shell is so hard that it resists all attacks. I know of no animal that under natural conditions can reach the edible core, or habitually use the fruit as food. The chacma was the one exception.

A troop we had an opportunity of observing travelled great distances to reach the isolated baobabs that are scattered through the *bushveld*. The country between the trees and the group of hills they inhabited was generally sandy and stoneless. They would pick the fruit and carry it for great distances to the foot of the hills, where the nearest stones were situated. The fruit is about the size of a small coconut, and the means the chacma adopted for carrying it to the hills was very interesting.

The adults generally carried four: one held in the teeth by the stalk on which it grew, one under the right arm, and one in each hand, the animal treading on those held in the hands. We never saw fruit carried under the left arm.

On reaching the hills, the fruit was placed on a flat rock and smashed with stones. My colleague noticed that in many instances, particularly among the younger individuals, great efforts were first made to break the fruit by hammering it on the rock by hand before a stone was used as a tool. Often all efforts would fail to break the fruit. It was then rolled off the rock and never touched again. In no other locality we visited where these trees grew did we come across this habit.

This group in the Magalakwên Valley had also acquired a habit which evinced just as high a conception of means to a definite end. They inhabited an isolated precipitous group of hills about five miles from the river. At the time we came in contact with them, a prolonged drought had dried up all the springs and drinking places in the hills. The nearest water they could reach was in the river bed; even here the only means of reaching it was by digging deep holes in the shifting sand. To get to the river bed they had to traverse a very exposed tract of country and cross a big road – the sort of journey to which the chacma is decidedly averse.

Very often the presence of human beings in the vicinity meant the baboons had to go without water for several days, or jeopardise their lives in reaching it.

But we found the hill-sides strewn with the chewed fibres of a bulb which proved to be that of a lily which contains a great deal of moisture. The bulb grows at a considerable depth, generally under stones or in soil which in drought is almost as hard as stone. A long rush-like leafless stalk grows out of the bulb and, after a number of twistings underneath and past stones, reaches the surface. A slight pull at this stalk detaches it from the bulb or breaks it deep down, and once it is detached it is almost impossible to find the bulb by digging.

Not only had the troop of chacmas discovered that this bulb would assuage thirst, but their method of reaching it showed that they fully appreciated the chief defensive attribute of the plant, and used the only means of overcoming it. In digging they were careful not to detach the stalk, but dug down round it, removing the stones, and so tracing it to the bulb. We never saw this bulb dug up or chewed anywhere else. In the vicinity of our own troop which we kept under continual observation, the plant was plentiful but it was never used by the baboons.

No less remarkable is the habit which has gained for the chacma a notoriety which was perhaps the chief reason that induced the Government to place a price on its head.

The animal is no flesh eater and no bird or mammal is ever killed for food, yet throughout the sheep districts of the Cape a great many young lambs are killed by baboons. The flesh is not eaten; their only object is to secure the curdled milk from the stomach. Here in the northern Transvaal the habit has not been acquired. No lamb is ever touched although a troop may be in contact with flocks of sheep almost daily.

Another troop which we had an opportunity of watching for a day had discovered a similarly 'rational' method of overcoming an environmental difficulty.

The presence of man in their neighbourhood had left them only one drinking place that could be visited with any degree of safety. This was a thermal spring. The water in the spring itself and for some distance downstream was too hot to drink, and a farmhouse, towards which the water flowed, made it dangerous for the baboons to go farther downstream.

But whenever they were satisfied that danger from the farm was not too threatening, they visited a spot where the water was drinkably cool. Very often this was impossible for long periods, as the farmlands extended right up to this place, and men were working in the vicinity. The baboons were then compelled to find water in the spring itself or immediately below it.

On the occasion that we observed their behaviour, about a third of the troop lined up along the water course below the spring, and each one scooped a furrow through the mud. When these furrows were filled with water, they moved farther up the hill-side to wait for it to cool.

The larger portion of the troop, agitated and uneasy, did not approach the water at all while these operations were going on. They awaited the results of their friends' labours at a safe distance. Those that took part in the operation of making the furrows consisted of about equal numbers of adults and young ones, and the difference in their respective behaviour was interesting. The adults went about the work quietly, methodically and phlegmatically, in the chacma manner, but the youngsters were greatly excited, jerking out the mud erratically, and frequently, when the hot water came in contact with their hands, uttering cries of rage.

After about an hour's wait on the hill-side, the whole troop again approached the water and commenced drinking out of the furrows. We noticed that only a very small percentage of these were used, and each baboon quietly waited his turn to drink.

The reason became apparent on closer examination. The mud was generally so soft that many furrows were soon obliterated and only those dug in the firmer area lasted long enough to cool the water. But even the majority of these could not be used, because they were made the wrong way. Whenever the furrow was dragged in a more or less down-stream direction, the continual entrance of hot water prevented cooling. A small proportion were scooped out more or less upstream or at right angles to the current, and in these the water cooled more quickly.

Whether the correct method was adopted by accident or design it was impossible for us to establish, since we had no opportunity of ascertaining whether the same individuals always adopted the same method of construction.

It needs no wide systematic knowledge of animal behaviour to recognise the great difference there is between habits such as these and the greatest adaptability conceivable in animals below the primates.

No other animal, under any circumstances, would or could behave in exactly this way, although it might prove difficult to define in other than general and meaningless terms the real nature of the difference. And without an appreciation of the significance of these peculiarities, it will be found difficult to form a satisfactory conception of the chacma's place in the scheme of mental evolution.

3
Phyletic and Individual Memory

WHAT IS THE ESSENTIAL NATURE of the mental process which the chacma thus translates into behaviour?

If one traces the shadowy occurrence of mental processes in non-primate mammals and their even more indeterminate appearance in birds, it is obvious that they are far less complex than in the primate. But such comparison does make it possible to form a clear conception of the real nature of the primate's mental process. If we look at the development of mental processes in the primate from one point of view – namely, in relation to the animal's struggle for existence – it is apparent that the process is fundamentally one of memory – memory in the human sense. It is not merely the memory of things in relation to locality, which even insects possess to a high degree. *It is the ability to memorise the relation of cause and effect.* It is the ability to accumulate what may be termed 'individual causal memories'.[1]

Whatever complexity this mentality may have attained in the primate, evidently the ability to accumulate individual causal memories was an early attribute singled out in the process of natural selection. In the chacma it has become dominant. Individual causal memory generally governs the animal's behaviour in relation to its environment.

Much of the behaviour of higher non-primate mammals is determined by 'instincts'. These are grouped round three great

---

[1] I do not think it is necessary to enter here into an abstract psychological analysis. References to behaviour will constantly be made which will make the conception clearer than attempted definition can at this stage.

psychic centres:

1) Sexual sense (reproduction and care of the young);

2) Fear of death (counteracting environmental dangers); and

3) Procuring of food.

These instincts are nearly always correlated to specific somatic modifications, as in insects.

Purely instinctive behaviour is quite determinate in character. The animal cannot voluntarily vary its behaviour. It meets the normal conditions of its environment in a certain definite way and cannot adjust its actions to overcome the hostile element in any unusual environmental occurrence.

Instinct in its purest form may therefore be described, from an evolutionary point of view, as an hereditarily established tendency to certain definite behaviour selected as a reaction to, and as most beneficial under, certain normal environmental conditions.

It seems hardly possible to speak of instinct in terms of the higher primate mentality. They are probably not related functions, and it is possible that pure instinct may be described as 'psychic' only in the sense that it employs, and in a similar manner, the same motor mechanism which the indeterminate mentality makes use of, and that both function through the central nervous system, though quite certainly in different centres.

Notwithstanding this, it would still be convenient to speak of instinct as 'phyletic memory'. There are many analogies between memory and instinct, and although these may not extend to fundamentals, they are still of such a nature that the term 'phyletic memory' will always convey a clear understanding of the most characteristic attributes of instinct.

In explanation of my definition of instinct, it must be pointed out that every set of muscular actions originally evolved in an organism by its environment must be either advantageous or disadvantageous. The organism that engages in such reactive muscular movements as would give it a better chance of surviving would retain that chance only by constantly making similar movements under similar conditions, and so certain definite actions become selectively established.

That seems to have been the evolutionary pathway of instinct.

Let us turn now to the operation of these two types of mentality – phyletic memory and individual causal memory – in nature. The analysis of mental behaviour which they respectively dominate will give a better idea of their real significance in the scheme of organic existence than would a great deal of explanation.

For this purpose, I shall select behaviour of three types, illustrating three different stages in the pathway of mental evolution:

1) An organism whose behaviour is entirely governed by phyletic memory; for whom the acquisition of a single individual causal memory seems an impossibility.

2) The behaviour of an animal in which phyletic memory is still dominant, but in whose action there is a suggestion of the new individual causal memory.

3) The behaviour of the chacma under analogous conditions; that is, a mentality in which the individual causal memory has assumed predominant control.

Behaviour Governed by Phyletic Memory

The road-making ants of Africa make pathways extending sometimes to a distance of 300 yards from the hole that leads to their underground nest. Along this road, worn smooth and hard by their tiny feet, a continual stream of workers passes. Those going are unladen; those coming back bear a seed.

These seeds are taken down into the nest and husked. The husks are then carried out and piled on the side of the hole opposite to that from which the prevailing winds come. These heaps of husks include those of all seeds – grass and shrub – found in the vicinity. The seeds, when extracted, are stored in an underground granary adjoining the nest.

Under certain conditions the ants can be deceived. If a long-used road is blocked and a new road drawn with some smooth hard implement, the workers, after a little hesitation, will follow the new road; and it is thus possible to lead them in any direction.

One species of road makers have a great aversion to crossing water; if a small trench is dug across the road at some distance from the nest and filled with water, they continue using the road, but they stop at the trench and become very excited, running backwards and forwards until eventually all the workers of the nest are collected at this spot – a confused and apparently aimless crowd.

Eventually a new road is made from the point at which the obstruction occurs. This new road and the direction in which it goes is apparently determined by the direction in which most of the workers happen to run in their excitement.

Several beginnings will be made by different groups thrown out from the main body. The biggest group will be the first to have a well-worn road, and this will be the one finally selected by all the workers. If the trench is dug near the end of a road immediately anterior to the place where the workers disperse to collect the seeds, and if this trench is filled with water, it often happens that a new road is not decided upon until a day has been spent in futile labour.

If a narrow bridge is placed across the water-trench directly in the middle of the old road, many, or perhaps all, workers in the collected crowd will one after another carefully test the bridge, but these attempts never go beyond an ant's length, so that the hind legs are still on the ground while the body is on the bridge.

The presence of the water in the trench is apparently the deciding factor, since they will cross a bridge with no water underneath. If a small soil-covered board is placed opposite the bridge, and ants are allowed to collect on it, it is possible to transport them across the trench in considerable numbers at a time.

Now a singular thing happens. All the workers thus transported across the line of water immediately travel to the end of the road and disperse to search for seeds. They come back to the road each carrying a seed, travel to the trench, and at once cross the bridge.

The operation is naturally far more risky for an ant struggling with a burden several times bigger than itself than it would be for an unladen ant. One can continue carrying the ants across the trench for a great length of time. By marking individuals with red paint, it can be ascertained that in the course of time the same ones are carried across repeatedly. If the waiting ants commence a new road, it is only necessary to obliterate it in order to concentrate them at the bridge again.

And after one's patience has been exhausted, their behaviour is still the same. Not one of those coming from the nest will ever cross the bridge, while those returning, encumbered with seeds, cross at once. It may be thought that holding a large seed in the mouth possibly prevents a sight of the water, and that the fearless crossing from the far side is due to this fact.

But this is not the case. If the seeds are taken from the ants just before they reach the bridge, they will continue their journey and cross just as readily as their laden fellows. And an ant will continue behaving in this manner after it has been carried over the water a great many times and crossed the bridge on the homeward journey.

The instincts involved will of course at once be apparent to the student of behaviour. On the far side of the bridge a double 'pull' is exerted. There is the instinct to secure food, and in addition there is the mightier homing instinct, which is sometimes stronger than the fear of death itself.

But the most remarkable thing is the apparent impossibility of teaching the workers that if there is no danger in crossing the bridge with a load, then there must be less danger in crossing it without one. If they could only learn that the bridge is safe to cross, it would constitute a causal memory of the simplest kind. But the ants cannot remember.

Suggestion of Individual Causal Memory

Game birds are protectively coloured and, as their main environmental danger comes from soaring birds of prey, they have developed by selection a tendency to crouch down in the grass and lie still. So strong is this instinct that when an unaccustomed danger threatens, the same method is adopted even when it increases rather than diminishes the risk. If the danger becomes too pressing, the bird will, as a last resort, try to save itself by flying or running to some new hiding- place.

For more than a hundred years game birds have been hunted with dogs and shot at as they fly, yet still they crouch and wait until man and dog get so close that their chance of escape is reduced to a minimum. The same bird may be wounded several times, but still he crouches and waits to be killed. However, a certain adaptation of behaviour to new conditions becomes apparent, even where these constitute a completely new experience.

In districts where birds are regularly shot, they fly farther, faster and scatter more widely than they do in districts where they have not been hunted, or than they would do when pursued by an eagle. There is, therefore, a causal memory. The bird remembers and its behaviour is to some extent dictated by that memory; but only to a small extent. The individual causal memory is not powerful enough to inhibit the phyletic memory which has become so highly disadvantageous under the new conditions.

Control by Individual Causal Memory

The third stage in the pathway of mental evolution is that of an animal in which the causal memory has become predominant. For this purpose I shall review our troop of wild baboons under conditions somewhat analogous to those illustrating the second type of mental behaviour.

For some five years they had had no experience of a man with a rifle. We had taught them not to fear man as such. The result was that they allowed any man with a rifle to come very close to them. During this time many babies had been born and had grown up who had perhaps never heard a gun fired, and certainly had never had the experience of having a gun fired at them.

When, towards the end of our period of observation, the troop was approached by two men armed with rifles, the older individuals at once uttered first the 'warning' and then the 'alarm' loudly and insistently; thereafter they stood not upon the order of their going. The youngsters, frightened by the cries of their elders, ran to their parents and a precipitate retreat was beaten. But when they realised that the two men were the only cause of all this commotion, they began to lag behind in their frantic race uphill and eventually stopped, watching the approaching men and the fleeing adults alternately. Two shots were fired at them. One young female was killed and another wounded. And that was the last time the scalp-hunters had an opportunity of shooting them in this manner.

For a long while the troop still tolerated unarmed human beings in their vicinity, but even this stopped when they had been caught once or twice by men with concealed rifles. Here we have behaviour shaped entirely by the new memory. The animal is burdened by no ready-made hereditary memory useful only in meeting customary events in its environment, and likely to become highly disadvantageous in the presence of new and unaccustomed conditions.

*

If I have perhaps unduly emphasised certain aspects of these three types of behaviour, it has been done only to make more apparent an essential attribute of the two great types of mentality in nature which they serve to illustrate.

It must not be thought that I am trying to prove the absence of individual causal memory in all animals outside the order of the primates. Its development, like all evolutionary processes, can be continuously traced as existing in different degrees in different species.

In insects and other lowly organisms it is almost entirely absent. Here the individual in its relation to its environment is completely dominated by hereditary memories only.

In the highest mammal, behaviour is, generally speaking, determined in this manner, but there is always an adumbration of the individual causal memory. However, it is only when we reach the primates that this soul, the individual causal memory, takes the predominant share in fashioning the behaviour of the animal in relation to its environment, and it is here that its real place in the scheme of mental evolution becomes clear.

Nor, on the other hand, is instinct – or phyletic memory – absent in the primate. Its activity is submerged by the soul of individual memory (*cf.* Freud's theories), and as we ascend higher up the scale to the anthropoids, the more noticeable does this submergence become. This process is correlated to definite organic modifications.

Two other facts must always be kept in view if we are to form any clear understanding of the chacma's mentality:

1) The new mentality is not in any sense an evolutionary product of instinct.

2) The new mentality does not take the place of the old – they exist side by side. Where the new mentality has become dominant, as in the chacma, the old mentality has become functionally submerged, but it is still there. In the primate the relation of the new mentality to the old one is of reason towards instinct.

The essential difference between these two types of mind – those largely governed by individual causal memory and those by phyletic memory – has been recognised by many thinkers, and various speculative attempts have been made to ascertain their selective cause. Professor Henri Bergson, for instance, writes in *L'Evolution Créatrice*:

> From the fact that instinct is always more or less intelligent it has been concluded that instinct and intelligence are things of the same kind, and that there is only a difference of complexity or perfection between them, and above all, that one of the two is expressible in terms of the other. In reality, they accompany each other because they are complementary, and are complementary only because they are different, what is instinctive in instinct being opposite to what is intelligent in intelligence.

I must confess that the concluding portion of this statement does not convey a very clear meaning to me. Nor can I quite agree with Professor Bergson's further assertion that these two types of mind are the outcome of two divergent pathways in evolution, and I shall attempt in the next chapter to arrive at an understanding of the probable evolutionary course of the new mind, as inferred from an analysis of behaviour.

In the meantime, I wish to emphasise that this speculation of Professor Bergson's seems irrefutable: One cannot speak of 'intelligence' as the evolutionary culmination of 'instinct', in the same sense as one would speak of the wing of the bird as the evolutionary outcome of the fore-arm of the reptile. It must always be remembered that we are dealing with functions and not with organs, and there can be no question that 'intelligence' is the function of a new organ – an organ quite different from that which governs instinct.

In the brains of primates and non-primates the organs of instinct and intelligence function in different degrees. It would therefore be incorrect to speak of 'intelligence' as a transformation of 'instinct', as one might perhaps speak of flying in the bird as a transformation of walking in the reptile, which is an evolved general function of the same transformed organ – in the case of instinctive and intelligent mentality, they are different functions of different organs.

Both types of mentality can therefore be recognised and distinguished in all the higher mammals in different degrees, but between the highest non-primate animal and the lowest primate there is a considerable hiatus in their relative activity. The low primate compared with the high non-primate seems somewhat beyond the mere transition stage. It is the position of the climber well over the top of the hill compared with the climber still on the nearer slope.

But it is quite possible that wider research may prove this hiatus to be more apparent than real.

It remains now to examine more closely the outstanding attributes of these two kinds of mind.

Instinctive Mentality

The term 'phyletic memory', which I have selected as preferable to 'instinct', seems to imply the existence of 'consciousness' in the human sense, since consciousness is a necessary adjunct of human memory. But I have already explained that by the term 'memory' I do not wish to predicate any identity with human memory. The term was selected only in view of certain striking analogies, and consciousness does not seem to be one of these.

A question which occurs sooner or later to every student of animal behaviour is: *Is there any consciousness in instinctive actions?*

It is of course essentially a matter of definition whether consciousness means either

> a) a mental picture of the end towards which behaviour tends, or
>
> b) a conception of cause and effect in the behaviour adopted.

One would at once be inclined to say that there can be no consciousness in instinctive action.

In the first definition, there can be no knowledge of an end outside individual experience. The weaver finch hatched under a canary commences, under certain conditions, to weave its beautifully patterned nest. It has never seen a completed nest. It has never gone through the difficult and complex process of tying the first straws, and yet it completes the nest in just the same way that the wild bird does. It is hardly conceivable that the bird can have any knowledge of the end towards which its labour tends. It cannot, as it works, have a mental picture of the completed work which it has never seen.

But we must not forget that such a conclusion is entirely anthropomorphic. We are judging the bird's mentality by our own. We cannot know a thing we have not experienced, and therefore we cannot prejudge the weaver finch. This reasoning has its weakness. We cannot weave a nest we have not seen, and yet the finch certainly does. In other words, if the tendency to such complex actions is hereditary, why cannot the mental picture also be hereditary?

And the matter becomes even more difficult when we consider complex instinctive actions performed by a 'conscious' being –

say, by a chacma or a human being. It is difficult to imagine a human being engaging in purposive actions where the purpose is unknown to him. It seems a contradiction in terms. And yet it does occur.

George McCall Theal mentions the wonderful homing instinct of the Bushmen. Young children taken by wagon great distances from their homes found their way back through pathless wildernesses. This same 'instinct' is present in most primitive peoples, and we had an opportunity here in Waterberg of examining just such a case of 'homing' in a descendant of the so-called 'vaalpens pygmies' that at one time inhabited the *bushveld* of the northern Transvaal.

A boy of about fourteen was taken on a roundabout journey of approximately 280 miles by road and rail to a new home which, because of an intervening large mountain range, was, in fact, no more than 40 miles away from his starting-point.

He had never been any distance away from his original home and certainly knew nothing of the surrounding country. Shortly after his arrival, he set out in the night and reached his old home two days later. His track was followed and it was found that his route was as nearly straight a line as the nature of the country would permit. It seemed an impossible performance.

Unfortunately, the intelligence of the boy was of a very low order. Careful questioning elicited no information other than the constantly repeated refrain: "I did not know where my home was, I ran away because I wanted to go home."

Here is another case. A baby chacma was reared for us by a lady in Waterberg, who took charge of it a few hours after birth. It was taken away from her when it was about eight months old, and transported a distance of 60 miles over two ranges of mountains through uninhabited country.

During the journey, it was shut up in a dark box and every means was employed to destroy its sense of direction. The little animal was passionately devoted to the human being who had taken the place of its mother. When released at its new home, it showed acute distress, running about restlessly and climbing to the tops of trees and houses, constantly calling for its human protectress.

Later in the day it became quiet but deeply melancholy, and refused to be comforted. It would take no food and ignored the overtures of the strange children around it, although it had never known playmates other than children.

Before daybreak the next morning, it had disappeared and six days later it reached its old home in the last stages of exhaustion and hunger, but showed the wildest delight when again embraced by its human foster-mother.

In both of these cases we clearly have purposive action towards an unknown purpose. At first glance it is hard to understand how a conscious human being can undertake a distinctly purposive action without a clear mental picture of the end towards which his action is directed and of each step to be taken to attain it.

But it is just this 'subconscious' behaviour of conscious beings which affords us perhaps the strongest ground for inferring that there is no 'conscious' mental picture in purely instinctive action.

It is quite certain that a conscious being can carry out highly complex purposive actions of which it is not conscious. There is no mental picture, no conscious reasoning, no memory involved in its performance. If such a mental process can occur in a mind ordinarily dominated by 'consciousness', then it is certainly conceivable that it will occur in the instinctive mentality.

Intelligent Mentality

But we are on surer ground when we come to consider the question of the mental concept of cause and effect in instinctive behaviour. It is certain that in the purely instinctive mind there is no conception of the relation between cause and effect in the world of the senses.

If, for instance, a purely instinctive animal is prevented from attaining the object of its actions, it will continue its futile efforts indefinitely, never realising that success is impossible. Even if the impediment is so simple that the most elementary conception of causality would at once make clear a method of overcoming it, that method will never be adopted it if entails a deviation from the customary course of action.

This, therefore, is one tangible example of the fundamental difference between the two types of memory: in the one there enters the element of causal comprehension, in the other it is absent.

And there is one other difference that is no less significant. Phyletic memories, as the name implies, are hereditary; causal memories are not. The ability to accumulate individual causal memories is of course transmitted, but the work done, the accumulated memories themselves, are never inherited by progeny from parents.

The weaver finch comes into existence latently equipped with all the complex memories necessary to overcome all the usual difficulties of its natural environment. Without instruction or individual experience, it knows how to build its nest and what material to use. It knows what its natural food is, where to look for it and how to secure it. It knows what to do to find a mate, and when the eggs are laid it incubates them and feeds the young on just the right food.[1] It knows what dangers threaten its existence,

---

[1] The finch is a seed-eater, but it feeds its young only on fish or grubs.

and if they appear, it knows exactly what to do to escape them. And it does these things without ever having seen them done.

The chacma seems a poor helpless thing when compared with this perfect hereditary knowledge of the weaver finch. Often it does not inherit even the most important environmental knowledge from its ancestors. Without instruction or individual experience, it does not know what food to eat and what to avoid; it just has no idea where to look for food. It does not know where to seek a safe shelter in the night or what to do to protect itself from the weather. It does not recognise real danger, a danger that has perhaps destroyed members of its race for a thousand years. Even the sexual sense is frequently not correctly orientated hereditarily. However, evolution has more than recompensed the chacma for this loss of hereditary memories.

It has become the fashion in certain popular 'natural history' books to ascribe all manner of human psychic attributes to animals. Among other marvels, the mother is described as teaching her young one necessary environmental knowledge. This is no doubt affecting and naturally appeals to deep human sentiments.

Nonetheless, I do not think that these stories, or other tales of the immediate memorising of complex new causes and effects, give a true picture of the animal's mind. Outside the order of primates there are no such processes in nature. It is only in primate behaviour that tradition first appears as a determining element.[1]

The young otter needs no instructions from its mother in the art of swimming and capturing fish, even if she were capable of imparting it, since it is born equipped with all the knowledge its mother possesses. It would be interesting to study this question

---

[1] [Recent studies show that in many non-primates – in particular predators – such learning is necessary. Marais, however, is of course correct concerning the superior capacity of primates. – R.A.]

of the inheritance of the instinctive mentality in higher mammals under experimental conditions.

However, we did have an opportunity of effecting a convincing comparison between the otter and the chacma in this respect, and a record of their respective behaviour makes clear the profound difference between these two animals as far as the inheriting of environmental memories is concerned.

Both baboon and otter were taken away from their mothers shortly after birth. The baboon was reared under our own supervision by a human foster-mother. The baby otter, whose captured mother died from wounds immediately after its birth, was placed among a litter of puppies and accepted by the bitch.[1]

Both were carefully kept apart from all contact with their own kind and all knowledge of their natural environment.

The otter was reared thirty miles from the nearest running stream. The only water supply in the vicinity was in a deep well, and it never, at any one time, saw more water than was necessary to quench its thirst. It never saw a fish or crab and was fed exclusively on raw meat.

When fully grown, it was taken for the first time to a river pool. It ran down to the water, smelled it and drank some. Then it struck the surface two or three times with its paw and immediately plunged in, diving, swimming and playing, just as a wild otter does. It had not been fed for some considerable time, and within half an hour it had captured a small fish and then a crab.

Our artificially reared baboon came from a district where its

---

[1] It is noteworthy that the baboon showed a deep and lasting devotion to its human parent-by-adoption. Even after a separation of three years, it immediately recognised her with the utmost joy and affection. The otter became quite indifferent to its foster-parent and 'relatives' the moment it could fend for itself.

natural food supply would have consisted almost exclusively of insects and wild fruit. The wild baboon obtains insects by turning over all the big stones in its line of march and is especially fond of the very abundant scorpions. This is a delicacy relished by wild baboons throughout South Africa, and they show great ingenuity in catching them. The scorpion is rapidly beaten about with the hand until half-dazed, and is then turned on its back by a flick of the fingers and seized by the legs.

In this position it cannot sting. The tail containing the sting and poison sac is carefully removed before eating. I have never seen a wild baboon stung by a scorpion during this process.

Among the wild fruit commonly eaten, there are several tempting-looking drupes and berries which are poisonous. Two species of fruit-bearing shrubs are remarkable because of the very close resemblance they bear to each other. These are the sandappel or the grysappel (*Parinarium capense*) and gifblaar (*Dichapetalum cymosum*). The fruits are very different in colour and size, but the plants themselves can hardly be distinguished from one another. The fruit of the gifblaar is bright red in colour and very tempting in appearance – but the plant secretes a poison of extreme virulence and the fruit is especially rich in the deadly substance.

The fruits of the two plants are far less conspicuously coloured. Both are edible and much esteemed by wild baboons and their human neighbours. I have never seen a wild baboon meddle with a poison plant or attempt to pick a poison fruit. They carefully avoid them. Quite small youngsters seem to know the danger. How the individual acquires this knowledge I am not sure, but not even in their case would I care to suggest purposive maternal tuition.

To this, its natural environment, our captive baboon was suddenly introduced for the first time when it was nearly full grown.

It had been deprived of food for long enough to make it extremely hungry, but although it was in the midst of unturned stones covering innumerable insects, it had no idea of turning them over, nor could direct suggestion awake any hereditary memory.

When a stone was turned exposing a number of scuttling beetles and scorpions, it leapt away in terror and for a long time it showed the greatest fear of a scorpion. After a great deal of coaxing it was at length induced to eat two from which the stings had been removed. It was then shown a third one under a stone and this time it greedily seized the insect and was promptly stung in the palm of the hand.

Each kind of wild fruit it handled with the greatest caution, first smelling it repeatedly and then nibbling small bits. When it was eventually introduced to the two plants mentioned, its confidence had grown to such an extent that it plucked and ate a grysappel without hesitation. There was just a little hesitation when it reached the poison plant. It picked a fruit and at once placed the whole of it in its cheek pouch and when it was prevented from plucking another, it at once commenced chewing the one it had. It was only then that the sense of taste must have come to the rescue, as the masticated fragments were at once ejected with every sign of distaste and fear, and never after that could our chacma be induced even to handle the leaves or fruit of the gifblaar.[1]

It becomes clear that, generally speaking, in the non-primate most memory necessary for it to exist in a certain definite

---

[1] All wild ruminants in the district where this plant grows avoid it instinctively, but domestic animals never learn its danger either by direct individual experience or through heredity and large numbers of cattle, sheep and goats are killed annually. Even the native cattle, which have probably had centuries of experience, eat it just as readily as the newly imported animals. Those that recover are often repeatedly poisoned by the plant, and dogs are sometimes also killed through eating the ripe fruit.

environment is phyletic and can remain latent for an indefinite time until it is called into activity through some suggestion from without. In the primate, little such memory is inborn.

In recapitulating the facts briefly, we must recall:

a) that the behaviour of all organisms is controlled by two different types of mentality;

b) that the foundation of the newer mentality is the ability to accumulate memories with causal comprehension;

c) that the one is not the evolutionary culmination of the other;

d) that phyletic mentality is inhibited by individual causal mentality and becomes inactive where the latter controls behaviour;

e) that the one is inherited as a complete mechanism for reacting to the customary environmental events;

f) that in the other the heredity extends only to the ability to accumulate individual memories, which renders possible beneficial reaction to all environmental events, whether customary or unusual; and

g) that both these types of mentality exist in different degrees of activity in all the higher mammals.

The great frontier between the two types of mentality is the line which separates non-primate mammals from apes and monkeys. On one side of that line behaviour is dominated by hereditary memory, and on the other by individual causal memory. The animal whose behaviour is dominated by the individual causal mentality inherits no directing memories other than those which control its behaviour during infancy. As the capacity for registering causal memories develops in the individual, so does the soul of phyletic memories become submerged.

All these stages that we see in nature in different degrees in different animals are convincingly portrayed in the ontogenetic, or individual, development of the primate soul.

It is known that the development, both embryonic and post-natal, of the organism is to a certain extent a recapitulation of the evolution of the species.

To this general rule, mental evolution affords no exception. The phyletic history of the primate soul can clearly be traced in the mental evolution of the human child. The highest primate, man, is born an instinctive animal. All its behaviour for a long period after birth is dominated by the instinctive mentality. The knowledge of its natural food supply and where to seek it is inborn. It has a knowledge and fear of falling, a phyletic memory of an arboreal past. It clings to the mother. It knows how to show distress by its cries.

But it has no memory, no conception of cause and effect, no consciousness. Then, as it grows, the new mentality slowly, by infinite gradations, emerges. The earliest sign of its dawning is the dim appearance of memory, and a mother's first glad exclamation in recognition of its coming has always been "My baby remembers!"

Its mind can register, vaguely and uncertainly at first, an individual causal memory. And it is here that the wonderful transition occurs; a transition which the phyletic evolution of the soul of the chacma exemplifies.

As the new soul, the soul of individual memory slowly

emerges, the instinctive soul becomes just as slowly submerged.

The one is not an outgrowth of the other. The individual soul seems gradually to overshadow the instinctive one. For a time it is almost as though there were a struggle between the two. The control is divided.

But in the end the new soul ousts the instinctive one from directing the mechanism which controls the behaviour of the individual, and assumes forever after the predominant place.

Surely in this manner and in no other, the higher primate soul evolved from that shadowy beginning of individual causal memory which we first clearly see in the higher mammals.

4

The Selective Cause

IN THE STRUGGLE for existence there must have been some strong advantage attendant upon individual causal memory to render possible its survival and triumphant evolution.

At the very outset of this investigation one is, therefore, met by the questions: How did this type of mind come to be selected? What advantages did it confer upon a species?

All transformations in organic matter, all modifications or organ function brought about by natural selection, are specialisations. That is to say, every modification is selected to react favourably under certain definite sets of natural conditions, and the organism in which such modification has been selected is limited, as far as that modification is concerned, to the special set of natural conditions which selected it. It is under these conditions only that it confers a real benefit upon the possessor.

Some specialisations may appear to be more extensive adaptations to natural conditions than others, but in any case it is only in a relative sense that a modification can be described as general. However widespread these conditions may be, the modification which embraces them is nonetheless a specialisation, and the limitation of the organism to the specific environment in which these selecting conditions exist is an inevitable condition.

No specialisations in nature are without an attendant number of disadvantages. Whether the specialisation continues and the attendant disadvantages are eliminated by selection of course depends upon their relative values in the struggle for existence.

But even the elimination of a disadvantage can only be effected by fresh specialisation. There is no such thing in nature as an organism in perfect accord with its environment. Even the highest adaptations are never ideal.

In ultimate analysis, this practical truth rests upon the certainty that all the laws of the inanimate universe are inherently hostile to organic life. The struggle of life is not, as it often appears in popular conception, merely the struggle of the organism against competing fellows.

From its inception, an organism struggles against opposing laws of matter which make for dissolution and the hindrance of growth. Organic evolution is at best but the line of least resistance. Selection is not so much the preservation of the fit as it is the destruction of the unfit. For the fit it is not so much a conquering invasion as a lucky escape.[1]

But it is, after all, the restriction to a definite environment which constitutes the main disadvantage which every adaptation drags after it. The more highly an organism is adapted to struggle against a certain set of natural conditions, the more effectively it is confined to the environment in which those conditions exist.

That is the universal law. The higher the adaptation to one environment, the more complete is the discord under a suddenly changed one. And since the natural conditions which select modifications are very often local – especially so with the higher mammals – the effect of such organic reactive adaptations is to impose often a local as well as an environmental limitation upon the possessors. It is, in fact, difficult to escape the conclusion that

---

[1] It is no doubt a conception of this truth which colours the thread of pessimism running through all recorded human thought; the conviction that, whatever the circumstances may be, the evil in existence must necessarily outweigh the good – as the sparks fly upward.

one great tendency of natural selection is to localise as well as to specialise.

It is a general law of nature that a suddenly changed environment means destruction, and it has been practically illustrated in numberless instances in this continent of rapidly changing natural conditions.

Reference has already been made to the inability of drought-affected otters to exist outside their natural environment even in the presence of abundant food for which they have not been specialised.

But the destruction of species is due on a far greater scale to the changed conditions attending man's advent. We have watched the dwindling and extermination of one great species after another, species that perished because they could not change their environment. The vast herds of bontebok (*Damaliscus pygargus*), blesbok (*Damaliscus albifrons*), springbok (*Antidorcas marsupialis marsupialis*) and black gnu (*Connochaetes gnou*) which at one time covered the great inland plains of Africa from horizon to horizon are on the verge of extinction or have vanished because they were unable to exist in the *bushveld* which lay as a harbour of refuge before them.

There is the same food, the same water, the same climate, and numbers of other great species could – and did – take advantage of this means of escape, and therefore still live. But these unfortunates were so highly specialised for the open plains that existence in the bush was impossible for them. One little factor – the treelessness of a locality – decided their fate.

In Waterberg it is possible at present to study this singular type of development closely. Large herds of springbok have always existed on the Springbok Flats. These flats are a small island of level, open country about sixty miles long by sixty wide, in a sea of *bushveld*. The open country and the *bushveld* merge almost imperceptibly into each other. In recent years the flats have become settled by farmers and the springbok are rapidly approaching extinction. A single step separates them from safety, and they cannot take it.

There is also the instance of a herd of giraffe driven by hunters into a treeless portion of the *veld* from which escape was difficult. Great herds of other big game, with which the giraffe commonly associates in the bush country, lived there. The pasturage was good (and the giraffe can feed on grass), water was plentiful, and yet within a few years the entire herd had perished.

It is sometimes a very slight and apparently insignificant morphological modification which decides the fate of an animal under a changed environment. Very often it is not even apparent, and this is certainly the case with respect to the springbok.

Organic modification, however, is never as powerful in limiting an animal to a certain environment as psychic specialisation. An instinct is in this respect tyrannous. Where it is a dominant factor in behaviour, an animal will overcome the fear of death itself – that strong determinant of action – rather than violate the inborn direction.

In nearly all the examples of non-primate behaviour I have described, this compelling power of hereditary memory will be apparent. Nature abounds with instances.

I might add to these a classic illustration, that of the Galapagos lizard (*Amblyrhynchus cristatus*) described by Darwin in his *Journal of Researches*. It is an amphibious animal and spends most of its time in the sea. It swims and dives with just the same ease and perfection that it moves on land. It feeds chiefly on seaweed and goes long distances out to sea to procure it. It can remain under water for at least an hour.

Now, it happens that all its natural enemies live in the sea. On land it is quite safe from predatory foes, or rather *was* until man arrived on the scene. So a hereditary memory was therefore selected and when danger threatened, the lizard had to reach the shore in order to be safe. If the animal is frightened on land, it will not enter the water but persist in trying to get inland. Even when cornered on the beach, it will allow itself to be caught and handled rather than enter the sea, and if, when caught, it is flung into the water, instead of swimming out to sea, it at once hurries back to land and climbs out on to the rocks.

But it is not necessary to multiply instances in order to make clear the power of hereditary memory. It is a thing that can be proved experimentally by very simple means in the case of every animal whose behaviour is dominated by this type of mind.

It will be seen that from the given facts, some very general rules are deducible:

- Below the order of primates an animal can seldom acquire an individual causal memory of sufficient force to inhibit the action of an hereditary one.

- Where an instinct is replaced or modified in nature, it is done not by the acquisition of an individual causal memory but by the evolution of a fresh hereditary memory through natural selection.

- It is only when we reach the order of primates that we find as a general process non-hereditary causal memory immediately replacing and modifying the action of hereditary memories.

Among the mammals the disadvantages attendant upon all specialisations are therefore far more irremediable in the case of instinct than one can conceive it to be where mere morphological modification is concerned. Even in cases where instinct is strictly correlated to organic structure, it seems evident that the bodily specialisation never so surely confines an animal to a limited environment as the attendant instinct. The one is, in the nature of things, rarely an insurmountable obstacle; the other cannot be overcome.

If now we picture the great continent of Africa with its extreme diversity of natural conditions – its high, cold, treeless plateaus; its impenetrable tropical forests; its great river systems; inland seas; deserts, rains and droughts; its sudden climatic change capable of altering the natural aspect of great tracts of country in a few years – all forming an apparently systemless chaos; and then picture its teeming masses of competing organic life, comprising more species, more numbers and of greater size than can be found on any other continent on earth – is it not at once evident how great would be the advantage if under such conditions, a species could be liberated from the limiting force of hereditary memories?

Would it not be conducive to preservation if under such circumstances a species could either suddenly change its habitat or meet any new natural conditions thrust upon it by means of immediate adaptation? Is it not self-evident that in a species far-wandering, whether on account of sudden natural changes, competitive pressure, or through inborn 'wanderlust', those individuals which could best and most quickly adapt themselves to the most varied conditions would be the ones most likely to survive and perpetuate the race; and that among species, one equipped for distant migrations would always have a better chance than a confined one?

Are not all the elements present to bring about the natural selection of an attribute by means of which a species could thus meet and neutralise one of the most prolific causes of destruction?

This is not advanced as a demonstrable theory. It is no more than an attempt to show that it is hardly possible to imagine conditions existing anywhere in nature at any time which would not in some degree tend towards the evolution of such an attribute.

If these present conditions are self-evidently likely to select it, how much more likely for instance, would not its birth and growth have been during the earlier history of the planet, during the Pleistocene period, when cataclysmic movements of its crust and great and repeated climatic changes still belonged to the usual and customary category of natural events?

What, then, would be the nature of the attribute which would have to be selected in order to realise this advantage? I think that I have made it clear that no mere somatic change, except in one respect, could attain it. No generalising perfection of hand or foot, nor the attainment of the upright position, nor the transformation of any function in any single organ could render a species immune from the danger inherent in suddenly changing natural conditions. It is not conceivable that it could have been attained in any other way than through a modification of the brain and its functions. In other words, the attributes selected had necessarily to be psychic.

The first step was the selection and perfecting of a mentality capable of individual causal memory. And the probable course of its evolution can be read in the stages of this mentality discernible in different existing species. From its first glimmerings in the lowliest vertebrate, through the high stage attained in the mammals, to its perfection in the primates, is reproduced the course it ran through the ancestors of the highest primates. The accumulated causal memories themselves were not hereditary. If they had been selected, it would at once have re-subjected a species to the disadvantage of limitation. The causal memories inherited by offspring would have reacted favourably only under the conditions which created them. To me this seems the only reason why accumulated causal memories were not selectively rendered hereditary just as instinctive ones were.

The next step was the obliteration of the mentality which inherits environmental memories. It will be seen later that where there is dual control – as in the lower monkeys – the analysis of behaviour invariably creates the impression of an apparent conflict, and it seems an inevitable conclusion that those individuals least burdened with phyletic memories are the ones most likely to survive. The least reflection will show that this must be so in the case of all animals in which the new mentality has taken shape as a determinant of action.

However, instead of heredity in the new environmental memory, another benefit was conferred. If the animal had had to acquire its own memories by direct individual experience only, it would have been subjected to many new disadvantages. It would individually have had to meet every environmental danger, it would have had to discover for itself every possible food supply and the best means for utilising it, before its memory could have been of any assistance. An average mammalian life-time would hardly have sufficed to adapt such an animal effectively to its environment.

If such a species possessed no hereditary environmental memories, each individual would have had to adapt itself to existence in this laborious fashion, no matter whether the environment into which it was born was an ancient or a recent one. Under such circumstances an animal with the most highly developed causal memory would hardly have had the same chance as the animal that enters upon life furnished with all the most essential environmental memories.

But inherent in the new mentality is the element of tradition. It is in reality only a consequence of the normal activity of the causal memory, but it has the result of enabling an animal to reap the benefit of the accumulated memories of its ancestors without the need of direct experience.

In the highest primate, articulate speech has enormously increased the scope and extended the benefit of tradition. The general effect of tradition therefore is equivalent to the general effect of hereditary memory. It is hereditary memory without the sting of limitation.

There was, of course, no sudden leap in the inception of the new mind. It was a thing of infinite gradations and stretches away through vast periods of time. The mills of God grind slowly and very uniformly. This 'despecialising' tendency is, in fact, as widespread as organic life itself.

It is only when we reach the order of primates, however, that the new mind emerges for the first time to take a great – or even a controlling – share in generally determining the animal's reaction to its environment.

And it is here that we encounter for the first time behaviour clearly under dual control. It is the same duality of control that we see in the human child when individual memory first becomes active. In the lower African arboreal monkeys this psychic doubling can be clearly studied in many different stages.

There are species where the individual grows up equipped with many important hereditary environmental memories while the causal memory is also active. For instance, a considerable number of vervet monkeys (*Cercopithecus aethiops pygerythrus*), reared in captivity, grew up with fairly complete hereditary memories. They all knew their natural food, where to look for it, and how best to utilise it.

They had a clear knowledge of environmental dangers. The larger African eagles – their worst natural foe – were instinctively recognised, and were guarded against in the only possible manner – that, is, by dodging under thick branches. Beasts of prey were also hereditarily recognised, but here hereditary memory was not as clearly directed as in the non-primate gregarious mammals. A donkey, for instance, when seen for the first time, caused just as much terror as a leopard.

The sexual sense was invariably correctly directed by hereditary memory.

There is, in fact, not a very great difference between them and the higher gregarious mammals as far as the activity of the instinctive mentality is concerned. But the difference becomes more than conspicuous when we come to consider the degree of development attained by the causal memory. The vervet is certainly not as 'clever' as the chacma. It is slower to accumulate individual memories and its comprehension of causality in the individual memory is not as perfect as in the chacma.

If in the vervet the 'dual control' is so equally divided that it is almost impossible to say to which side the balance swings, then it is in the chacma that the process of submergence of the instinctive mentality first becomes clearly apparent. Here for the first time individual memory assumes dominant control of the mind.

And there is a further singular difference between the chacma and the vervet in respect of the instinctive mentality. In the vervet there is great uniformity of instinctive behaviour; in the chacma there is great individual variation: that is to say, all the artificially reared vervets showed the same degree of hereditary memory.

In the chacma, individuals are found that are almost as completely equipped with hereditary memories as the vervet; but a large percentage lack even the most essential ones. Generally speaking, it is the 'clever' chacma that is without phyletic memories. The 'stupid' ones are sometimes highly instinctive.

5

Addiction and Depression

THE HABITUAL USE of poisons for the purpose of inducing euphoria – a feeling of mental well-being and happiness – is a universal remedy for the pain of consciousness. Euphoric intoxication is of especial interest in this study because of convincing proof that there exists in the chacma a state of mind similar to that which induces the use of euphorics in man.

I do not know of any human race, savage or cultured, which has not developed, or acquired from other races, the habit of using some poison, generally of vegetable origin, for the purpose of creating euphoria. There is hardly an exception to the rule that every race has discovered in their own habitat some such poison, or a method of manufacturing one.

The only exception would, of course, be the Arctic races, but even they have all, at one time or another, acquired intoxicants from their neighbours in both East and West. On the other hand, I do not know of any species of animal under natural conditions that has discovered or acquired a knowledge of this kind and so formed a definite new habit. The one exception in this country is the chacma.

The poisons most widely used by man are opium and alcohol, but a list to include all the vegetable substances that are so employed throughout the world would fill a respectably large volume. All of them have one property in common: the first, and chief, physiological effect is a temporary feeling of happiness which wears off as the poison is eliminated by the system. Among savage races, alcohol is used for one purpose only: to get drunk. But even among the most highly cultured European races, alcohol was, within the memory of man, used for the same purpose by all classes of the community – to get drunk, completely and unequivocally. The disrepute into which drunkenness has fallen among the higher classes in Western civilisation is a recent development.

As to the purpose in the use of all such poisons, I do not think there can be any question. A state of mental exhilaration or happiness is sought by the individual which he does not otherwise possess. The euphoria of intoxication replaces a condition of unhappiness varying in intensity in different individuals.

But it is not every case of mental suffering which seeks relief in intoxication. It still remains mainly a matter of temperament. And even in cases where the pain of consciousness is acute and the temperament favourable, there may be sufficient correctives in the environment to rival the poison as a remedy. When these exist and when, in addition, a clear perception of the danger is temperamentally possible, the powers of subjective inhibition may be strong enough to keep the temptation at bay.

It is often said that a man 'takes to drink' on account of some disadvantageous change in his condition. I think in such cases the determining factor is none the less the pain of consciousness that was present and which became dominant by the removal of what had been a continuous restraint. Men drink on happy occasions, too, because they have the assurance that in this manner all vestiges of mental gloom will be lifted and they will attain a state of pure joyousness more in accordance with the environment.

The supreme danger which lies in the use of intoxicants as a cure for mental suffering and which often renders the remedies worse than the disease is of course the morbid organic changes resulting from habitual use. Cessation of use causes what are known as symptoms of abstinence, of a severity and painfulness proportionate to the usual dose and the duration of the habit.

These symptoms are always painful, and a dose of the poison invariably affords relief from their immediate effects.

Long-continued habits, therefore, set up in time a double 'pull' – the craving for the characteristic euphoria and a dread of the painful symptoms of abstinence. It is to those temperaments in which pain is a predominant element of consciousness, and in which some quality of suffering is inseparable from thought, that alcohol and all joy-creating poisons constitute the greatest threat. Under its influence the individual experiences a complete respite from intolerable suffering.

The Mighty Mahmud, Allah-breathing Lord,
That all the misbelieving and black Horde
Of Fears and Sorrows that Infest the Soul
Scatters before him with his whirlwind Sword.

In such cases life becomes a continual struggle to render permanent by excessive use the very fleeting happiness these poisons bring, or even to attain a higher state of mental exaltation, an endeavour which can never be realised. There is continual alternation between the deepest gloom of abstinence and a mental state, when drunk, which through continuous use of intoxicants begins to resemble sluggish mental anaesthesia rather than positive happiness: but even this psychological narcosis is a respite and becomes to the individual preferable to the normal condition of suffering.

It is in such cases that all the bonds of civilised life are eagerly snapped, where the strongest springs of human conduct – love of friends and relatives, position, honour – are restraints more powerless than plumed reeds to stop the whirlwind in its course. Everything held priceless in normal psychic life is carelessly cast into the maelstrom. The sufferer drifts into a vicious circle and, like the scorched fly, spins in vain upon the axis of his pain. The black horde that normally infests the soul is replaced by an ordered league of deadlier foes against whom the Allah-breathing Lord now in vain unsheathes his whirlwind Sword.

Proof that it is some type of mental gloom which induces the use of euphoric poisons is further afforded by the strength and universality of these habits among peoples in whom melancholy of temperament is a definite racial characteristic. The Russian peasantry and the Chinese might be cited as outstanding examples of nationalities whose pessimism and lack of joyousness are the first traits to engage the attention of a stranger, and there are few other races upon whom habits of intoxication have gained so strong a hold.

In this country, the Bushmen seem the embodiment of mental misery. It is amusing to read today the observations of earlier investigators in this respect. Many of them were in doubt as to whether these people could cough or sneeze, but they seemed to be quite sure that they did not know how to laugh![1]

Even their pleasures are sad beyond words. Their songs are dirges, their dances funeral processions and their favourite music a monotonous wail of misery. And never was a race so quickly and effectively devastated by habits of intoxication.

---

[1] See Martin Heinrich Carl Lichtenstein: *Reisen in Südlichen Africa*.

They had a poison of their own – a wild hemp widely smoked by the yellow races[1] in South Africa. But *dagga* had apparently created a high degree of tolerance or was not virulent enough to suit their taste. They seized upon the white man's intoxicants, alcohol and tobacco, with avidity. Lichtenstein described their method of using tobacco in his time. They drew the smoke from a tube of antelope bone and swallowed it. It was not inhaled and exhaled from the lungs as cigarette-smokers do these days. By swallowing, the smoke was passed directly into the stomach, so that a whole pipe full was consumed without any escaping from the mouth. It quickly induced profound unconsciousness succeeded by violent sickness, during which the swallowed smoke gradually escaped, each patient (if so he can be named) being assisted in turn by the recovered members of the party.

The yellow races of the more northerly areas (Hottentots, Griquas, Korannas) have gone a step further in the use of tobacco as an intoxicant. The tolerance set up by a century of abuse has rendered all the usual applications quite ineffective and they have now acquired the habit of consuming the thick viscous oil concentrated in old tobacco pipes. The oil is placed behind the lower lip and gradually swallowed with the saliva. It seems almost incredible that sufficient tolerance could be created for the body to become proof against such doses of a poison so active and deadly.

---

[1] [Marais refers to the indigenous light-skinned people – the Bushmen and the Hottentots – who inhabited Southern Africa before the darker-skinned negroid tribes pressed down from the north a few centuries ago. Their origin is unknown, but seems to have no relation to Asia. Few pure Hottentots can be found in our time although through crossing with the white population they form the considerable people known as Cape Coloureds. The Bushmen survive only in remote areas of the Kalahari desert. – R.A.]

It will readily be imagined what effect alcohol had upon a race so strongly predisposed to its use by every trait of character and every circumstance of their lives. While it was still possible for them to procure brandy from traders without any restriction, this constituted the chief, if not the only, article of commerce supplied by the whites in exchange for the products of the industry and skill of these cattle-breeders and hunters.

So powerful was the craving for drink that every restraint went by the board. They bartered not only their wealth, their cattle and skins for brandy, but their means of livelihood as well. When all else had gone, ploughs, wagons, and guns were offered.

In the times of desperate need, the quantity of brandy they received in exchange was of small importance, so long as it was sufficient to cause complete intoxication. As a last resort, they invariably offered their wives and children, and it is well-known that numerous Koranna 'apprentices' were so procured by brandy-traders in former days.

There was the same utter want of restraint in consuming the fiery liquids they purchased so recklessly and paid for so dearly. The visit of a trader to a *stat* was invariably followed by numerous deaths directly due to acute alcohol poisoning.

The race has almost disappeared. As a united nation they exist no longer, and I do not think that any South African historian of the future will hesitate to ascribe this rapid decline not so much to the hostile invasions and conquests of white and black foes as to the destructive effects of alcohol.

Intoxication in the Chacma

On the central plateau of the district of Waterberg near the source of the Palala River we came on one occasion into contact with a very large troop of baboons which we kept under observation for a considerable time. Our interest was due to the fact that we had been told that they had discovered for themselves a method of intoxication. We had previously heard numbers of stories to the same effect about other troops, so we took this opportunity, which looked promising enough, to ascertain if possible the truth of the matter. Unfortunately, the circumstances were against us and in the end we were unable to settle our doubts definitely. But the observations are worth recording.

This troop had no less than five widely separated sleeping places. They were extremely wild, and the moment our attention aroused their suspicions they trekked away into the most inaccessible parts of the Hangklip Mountains, from the precipices of which they maintained a careful watch on all our doings. Systematic observation under such circumstances was quite impossible.

On this plateau and on the surrounding mountains of this region grows a shrub-like tree belonging to the family *Cycadacoae*. It is a rare plant and seems to have a very limited habitat. The leaves are a vivid green, and the tree bears a small plum-like fruit of a dull red colour when ripe. Among local people this fruit has the reputation of being extremely poisonous. In spite of a great scarcity of food at the time, we found no direct evidence that it was being eaten by either birds or insects.

Some trees, however, had been stripped bare and it was evident that these had recently been visited by baboons and there was every reason to believe that they had plucked the fruit. We were assured that several troops of baboons in the region were in the habit of eating this fruit, even during times of plenty, and that the animals became 'drunk' after such a feast. The drunkenness manifested itself in staggering gait, inability to move quickly, and in utter carelesness of danger, all of which rendered them, at such time, an easy prey to the hunters' dogs and rifles.

We saw none of this behaviour personally, and experiments with the fruit on captive baboons had negative results. Neither long starvation nor any other enticement would induce our chacmas to eat. Both in smell and in flavour it was 'sickly' and unpleasant. The pulp of two of the ripe fruits killed a full-grown cock in about twenty minutes.

About a year subsequent to our first visit, three little children in the Palala district ate some of the fruit, and the relatives sent to us for assistance. We reached the farm-house about four hours after the fruit had been eaten. Emetics and several other home remedies (which were mostly utterly useless if not actively harmful) had been administered.

The eldest of the three children – a girl of ten – had died in convulsions about an hour after eating the fruit. It is possible that some of the innumerable remedies administered may have had a share in bringing about the fatal result. She was described as having fallen into a deep and quiet sleep just before death. The convulsions came on suddenly; none of the three children had previously shown any convulsive symptoms.

Of the other two (a boy and a girl of eight), the boy had recovered. He was still sick and lethargic when we arrived, but was able to give an account of the incident. He told us that they had each eaten two of the fruits, but the result of the emetics seemed to show that this was untrue and that many more had been eaten.

The second girl was comatose and all efforts to rouse her proved unavailing at first. She was insensible to pain, the face was flushed, the pulse full and slow, the breathing deep, regular and very slow. The pupils were dilated and insensitive to light. She remained unconscious for about six hours and had to be kept awake forcibly for some time after she had regained consciousness. It was about thirty hours before she had recovered sufficiently to be pronounced out of danger. There were no convulsions.

The symptoms seemed to be those of a narcotic poison. Whether there was any euphoria it was of course impossible to ascertain from the children, and it must be borne in mind that even in known euphoric poisons the pleasant feeling is generally experienced only after considerable use and after a certain degree of tolerance has been set up.

Our own troop of wild baboons very often chewed and sucked the roots of a semi-aquatic plant which was generally known as poisonous. It was frequently used in small doses by the local people as a combined emetic and purgative, and although we never heard of a case of fatal poisoning, I can well believe, judging from its effects when used as a medicine, that a large dose would cause death. I cannot believe that its habitual use would induce euphoria.

Why the baboons ate it is a mystery. In taste it was extremely nasty and its immediate physiological effects were not those which one commonly associates with joy of mind and body. But I have already referred to this inexplicable habit, which the chacma has, of chewing absolutely 'inedible' plants and leaves – substances which no human being could use except as a punishment or an act of self-sacrifice. But it must be born in mind that to other races many of the delicacies we white people eat and drink are equally unpleasant, and the reason why we enjoy them is just as mysterious to them as the strange tastes of the chacma are to us.

It will be seen that I am by no means prepared to say, as a result of my own observation, that the chacma has discovered poisons which it uses for the purpose of euphoric intoxication in the same way that man does, but my knowledge of the general character of the animal, and its habits in captivity and under natural conditions make me strongly inclined to believe that the statements made to us and referred to above are true.

But whether or not it has acquired such habits under natural conditions, one thing is certain: in captivity the chacma has a powerful psychological predisposition to the use of intoxicants, and it may be argued that this predisposition is due to the same cause as in man – namely, some kind of suffering inseparable from the new mind which, like man, it has acquired in the course of its evolution.

The South African baboon in captivity is singularly like the Bushman in its predilection for tobacco and alcohol. It needs little observation to convince one that the taste for tobacco is not instinctive and hereditary. Wild baboons certainly never make use of it even where there is every opportunity for doing so. I have often seen baboons pass through tobacco fields daily to reach mealie lands and orchards, but I never saw them touch the plants, and this, I think, is the general experience of residents in Waterberg.

Our own wild troop were for a long period constantly within reach of a number of tobacco plants that grew in the vicinity of our huts, but they never touched them. In captivity, on the other hand, the chacma's taste for tobacco is so common that it was almost impossible for us to determine when any particular individual had first acquired it. All captive baboons beg for tobacco and eat or chew it with all the zest of a long-established habit. One old male showed a great liking for pipe-oil similar to the craving of the Hottentots. He had taught himself to scratch the oil out of a pipe-stem with a blade of grass which he then cleaned on to a piece of paper, rolled up and chewed.

Every observer of the South African Bushmen describes their craving for tobacco and alcohol in the same terms, and all that has been said of them could, as a matter of fact, be applied word for word to the chacma. The desire for tobacco, for instance, is always spoken of as an inborn one. Of course it is not so – but, like the chacma, the individual so immediately succumbs to the appeal of this poison that it always appears to the observer as if the inclination had existed all along and was not created purely by experience.

With regard to alcohol, the Bushmen required some little teaching, as there was always an initial aversion to the taste, but it is a common saying, based on the experience of the white races in South Africa, that a Bushman, without any previous knowledge of alcohol, becomes a drunkard the moment he once clearly experiences its intoxicating effect.

As a result of a great many experiments on the chacma, the following can be stated as a general rule to which there were, in our experience, no exceptions: an adult male chacma[1] that has once taken alcohol in sufficient quantity to experience its euphoric effect ever after evinces a strong craving for it.

---

[1] As a general rule, the female is less susceptible than the male – that is to say, it takes longer experience to establish an absolute and enduring craving for alcohol.

There is a great difference between the reaction of the chacma to alcohol and that of all other animals below the primates which we had an opportunity of studying. We tried the effects of the continued administration of alcohol on the following animals: vervet monkey (*Cercopithecus aethiops pygerythrus*), warthog (*Phacochoerus aethipicus aethiopicus*), saddle-backed and maned jackal (*Proteles cristatus*), and klipspringer (*Oreotragus saltator*). The spirit used was absolute alcohol diluted with water in such different proportions as the circumstances of each individual case seemed to indicate.

The first rule which we deduced from these experiments was that it is impossible in any of these animals to create a craving or even an inclination for alcohol by its repeated administration so long as the time interval between the doses is long enough to avoid any chronic organic disturbance. It makes no difference how long the administration is continued. The animal's natural distaste for alcohol seems to increase rather than to decrease with the continuance of forced doses.

If, however, the quantity of alcohol is gradually increased and the interval between doses diminished until a marked tolerance has been set up, then, if the administration is suddenly stopped, so-called symptoms of abstinence very similar to the human symptoms under analogous circumstances may manifest themselves. There is a general systemic disturbance. The digestive process becomes abnormal and there is a rapid falling off in condition and weight. Restlessness and sleeplessness are invariable accompaniments. In some cases, tremors involving the entire nervous system are an initial symptom, and continual whimpering cries indicative of persistent pain continue, subsiding only with the organic symptoms.

Now, all these symptoms of organic suffering can be arrested at any time by a dose of the poison which caused them, and it is possible in the vervets and jackals to create a memory by repeating the process. The animal can be made to remember that a dose of alcohol will end its suffering immediately. It can be made to associate, under such circumstances, the taste and smell of alcohol with the cessation of pain. Once you have created and fixed that memory, you have also created a temporary craving for alcohol which lasts as long as the symptoms do.

It will be seen that the presumption that the chacma is in some degree liable to the same quality of suffering which is undoubtedly an attribute of human consciousness rests upon more certain grounds than the mere fact that it exhibits the same degeneration of certain mental processes that man does, processes which assume in human consciousness the appearance of being the whole and only cause of this quality of psychological suffering. That would be a very slender foundation for such a theory if it stood alone; because at the very outset one is met by the objection that it is more than possible that this appearance of cause-and-effect is entirely fallacious. In other words, that the degenerate mental processes and organic states which I have discussed are not the cause of the pain of consciousness but are far more probably, together with the latter, the effects of a common and more deeply seated mental mischief.

If the craving for alcohol in the chacma is a strong proof of this theory because it resembles in all ways the same psychological process in man, and in this respect stands unique in the animal world, then the existence in the animal of the human 'hesperian depression' would, to my mind, be an equally strong one. Here, too, one has to deal with a mental state apparently characteristic of man alone, and quite evidently an attribute of his consciousness.

Hesperian Depression in Man

Normal mental pain in man, generally speaking, is tidal in character. With sunrise or during the early morning it is at its lowest ebb, to reach its highest flow in the evening about the time of the setting sun. In great cities and in the midst of strenuous civilisations it is difficult to study the nature of this tidal swing because of the infinite influences which all tend to modify the normal manifestation, and also because of the many remedies which man, when congregated in great numbers, devises to counteract the diurnal crisis. It is just when under more natural conditions the psychological process would assert itself, and become clearly apparent, that the lights flash on in houses and streets, that a thousand places of amusement stand out most enticingly. It is then that man, assisted by an artificial environment created, if unconsciously, nonetheless certainly to that end, can shift the centre of mental attention completely.

It is not

... in luxurious cities, where the noise
Of riot ascends above their loftiest towers,
And injury, and outrage: and when night
Darkens the streets, then wander forth the sons
Of Belial, flown with insolence and wine... [1]

where normal Hesperian depression can best be measured and appreciated. It is under more natural conditions, where all these artificial remedies are wanting, that this depression appears as a clearly recognisable attribute of human mentality.

On the *veld* it is known and discussed by both Europeans and natives with the same familiarity that any other universal common mental state is recognised and discussed.

---

[1] Milton, *Paradise Lost*

It is very remarkable and interesting that the depression reaches a climax immediately after sunset and endures for a short period only. When darkness has once settled, the mental condition changes entirely. Among the natives these phases are very noticeably translated into behaviour. An air of quietness and dejection falls upon the village just about sunset. The men and women go listlessly and mournfully about such tasks as still remain to be done. The old people gather in sheltered corners or about the fireplaces, quite silent. Conversation ceases. No song is heard and no sound of musical instruments. It seems very much like the dejection of utter physical weariness.[1] The little children are by no means exempt. All laughter ceases, the games come to an end and there is a general tendency to creep closer to the mothers and elders; an apparent craving for protective fondling and endearments.

As the night falls, the scene changes. The fires are newly made. Conversation and laughter are heard once more. Songs and the sound of music arise and under the brightening stars the young people congregate at the dancing place, where the last vestiges of dejection and weariness vanish.

It is interesting to note that here, too, there is a general tendency to describe the depression as the product of reason. The more uncivilised natives ascribe it to a fear of approaching darkness. It is during the dark hours, they suggest, that wizards go forth to create misery and distress; to sow disease and death among their defenceless neighbours. It is then that the spirits of the dead have the opportunity of manifesting themselves in a manner profoundly malevolent to the living; and other evil powers

---

[1] All these signs are, of course, absent in a village where beer has been made and is being drunk.

of unknown origin have all to wait for the night to attain their wicked purpose.

Small wonder, therefore, they say, that human beings should become thoughtful and distressed at the time of approaching night. Why the condition should change for the better when darkness has actually arrived, they are (like their more civilised neighbours) quite unable to explain, or the explanation is childishly illogical.

The Boers explain the condition, as might be expected, on more abstract grounds. The coming of night suggests the approach of death; the utter futility of human life; the distressing certainty of the end of all things; and the helplessness and paltriness of man. Of all this, the setting sun is a recurring emblem.

If this state of mind is not easily recognisable in the midst of great civilisations, it must not be assumed that it is absent. In some degree it is universally experienced and has been an attribute of human mentality since the beginning of history. In the sun-stories of the dawn of civilisation the daily death of the great luminary appears as typifying the feeling. In poetry and art it reappears throughout the history of human culture. No artist has fixed upon canvas the colour and light and atmosphere of this special time of day without in some degree imbuing his composition with the 'sadness that comes with the evening'. Even under the chisel of the sculptor it has found expression in every age in innumerable stones.

In religion all pronounced and common human psychological phases are represented in some form. This 'evening melancholy', which would naturally be accentuated in the religious temperament, appears magnificently in the stately formalities of both Eastern and Western Christian Churches. In all religious

literature man's helplessness in the presence of an evil against which his own inward means of defence are so clearly powerless is constantly expressed:

> *Abide with me; fast falls the eventide...*

It is in poetry, song and music, however, that this psychological process has come to striking utterance. How many 'nocturnes' are there which owe their popularity chiefly to the profound melancholy which the artist was able to express in beautiful words, colours or tones, and which finds an instant echo in most human souls? Very often it is the powerful suggestion of death which is accepted and expressed as the cause:

> *The curfew tolls the knell of parting day...*

But even when it is the beauty of the evening which makes the stronger appeal, it is seldom that that beauty can be expressed without revealing its inherent melancholy. One remembers as an example of this Milton's lines from *Paradise Lost* which Newton described as unparalleled in verse:

> *Now came still evening on, and twilight grey*
> *Had in her sober livery all things clad;*
> *Silence accompanied...*

Hesperian Depression in the Chacma

In few phases of behaviour did our troop of baboons appear to us more human-like than in the unquestionable expression of this 'evening melancholy'. They generally reached their sleeping place some time before sunset, to spread over the banks and rocks of the gorge-stream. Groups would collect in several shady spots and one could hear the animated chatter of the elders above the sound of the perturbed waters. Among the younger members of the troop this was the favourite time for mating, for strutting and boastful calling, and very frequently for romping games.

It was especially the hour of the little ones. The favourite playground was a shallow rock pool with an earth slide on one side and a huge branch-swing that must have been used by their ancestors for generations, to judge from the mirror-like polish imparted to the bark. It was during the hour before sunset that games were indulged in with the utmost joyousness. Incessantly their happy laughter and shrieks of excitement and delight awoke the echoes of the great shadowy gorge, while the older fathers and mothers sat watching the activity.

With the setting of the sun and the first deepening of the shadows a singular transformation came over the entire scene. Silence fell upon them gradually. The 'talking' ceased. The little ones crept affectionately into the protecting arms of their mothers. The romping young folk joined different groups, generally on the higher flat rocks from which a view could be had of the western horizon. The older ones assumed attitudes of profound dejection, and for long intervals the silence would be unbroken except for the soft whimpering complaints of the little ones and the consoling gurgling of the mothers.

And then from all sides would come the sound of mourning,

a sound never uttered otherwise than on occasions of great sorrow – of death or parting. I do not think there is any possibility of mistaking the state of mind which determines this behaviour – even by one not well acquainted with the character and ways of the animal. One need only compare them with a native village under the same conditions to realise beyond any shadow of doubt that you have here a representation of the same inherent pain of consciousness at the height of its diurnal rhythm. In the case of the chacma the condition also disappears with the settling darkness. When the troop finally moved on to the *krans* or to the entrance of the sleeping cave, the games were resumed and sometimes on moonlit nights continued for several hours.

In the presence of these proofs, it is hardly possible to avoid the conclusion that the chacma suffers from the same attribute of pain which is such an important ingredient of human mentality, and that the condition is due to the same cause.

6

Submerged Instinctive
Attributes in Man

IN RECENT YEARS so considerable a literature has arisen about the 'Subliminal Soul' that there are few readers who will not have some idea of the present state of knowledge regarding this strange psychological process in man. In arriving at this knowledge, however, considerable allowance must be made for the mysticism which has always found a happy hunting ground in this half-explored country where even the angels tread fearfully.

True subconscious behaviour in man is really illustrated by a psychic process which has certain definite characteristics. But before considering these, it would be as well to have a clear conception of the difference between normal unconscious and abnormal subconscious behaviour.

Normal unconscious behaviour is determined by a mental process which occurs as a usual and constant manifestation in nature and which is of immediate benefit to the organism.

Abnormal subconscious behaviour is an unusual occurrence which not only is not directly beneficial, but is so often allied to pathological conditions, that, if not a disease itself, it certainly always appears suspiciously like a symptom of disease. It can occur only under conditions of the conscious mind which are not usual and which certainly are not beneficial.

The most common type of normal unconscious behaviour is exemplified in motor habit, which in man is clearly a phyletic survival of his pre-conscious period. A man learning to ride a bicycle or to do a sleight-of-hand trick or any unusual combination of muscular movement has in the beginning to direct his centrifugal impulse with continual conscious mental effort towards the different muscular movements constituting the action.

The nervous impulse wears for itself a smooth channel, just as water does through soil, and the movements gradually become quicker and more perfect. The mental effort becomes proportionately smaller until eventually the most complete muscular movements take place without any corresponding representation in consciousness.

This 'learning to do a thing' is a property common to all muscular movements throughout nature. The same 'effort' is needed in minds which are not 'conscious' in the human sense. The human baby learning to bring food to its mouth or the more difficult process of bipedal walking, a bird learning to fly or an animal to run – all exhibit a similar struggle.

The same difficulty is encountered in teaching an animal a trick which requires any unusual combination of muscular movements. As the movements become more perfect the effort becomes less apparent and in the end disappears.

Unconscious motor habit is what Henry Maudsley terms the memory of the spinal column. In man this unconscious muscular movement is subconscious only in the sense that it is not at a specific time consciously repressed; but it was at one time, and so the movement can voluntarily be called back into consciousness.

Another alleged manifestation of what is often spoken of as 'subconscious' is the so-called 'repressed thought'. Those who accept Sigmund Freud's psychology as true in substance hold that there are many 'repressed thoughts' in human mentality which can, and often do, become pathologically potent. These thoughts are – to use Freud's own word – *Bewusstseinsunfähig*.

The meaning one attaches to the word – 'incapable of becoming conscious' – is, however, not quite borne out by his teaching. These repressed thoughts were at one time either conscious or hovering dimly on the frontier of consciousness, and were then thrust into outer darkness, where, safely hidden, they work their evil spells.

Such, I take it, is the real meaning of Freud's theories. And when one comes to consider the aim of his teaching, the word *Bewusstseinsunfähig* becomes even more inappropriate. His aim is to heal, and the healing is rendered possible by the circumstance that these repressed thoughts and tendencies can undergo a rebirth in consciousness – with the obstetric assistance of the psychoanalyst – and in this reappearance; they lose their evil potency.

If therefore, this theory is true it would appear, on his own showing, that the repressed thoughts are outside consciousness in much the same sense that a forgotten word or event is outside memory. The possibility of their recall, if not voluntarily then by means of outside suggestion, always exists, just as the unconscious muscular movements can at any time be made conscious voluntarily. If these 'repressed thoughts' do exist, they cannot be classified as 'subconscious' in the sense that I understand.

True subconscious purposive behaviour in a pure form has one feature which serves at once to distinguish it from all other types of mental activity.

It is this: *the subconscious actions never were conscious and can never under any circumstances become conscious in a true sense*. The subject may become aware of the results of his subconscious actions, and he may even – by post-hypnotic suggestion, for instance – be made aware of the subconscious actions themselves; but he becomes aware of them in just the same way that a spectator becomes aware of the actions of another person. They are not *his* actions. They certainly do not originate in his own normal conscious individuality. That is what I wish to be understood by subconscious purposive behaviour in its purest form.

There are intermediate types to which this description may not in strictness seem to apply, but it is nevertheless the common-sense view to regard all these occurrences as manifestations of one and the same psychosis.

In man, subconscious purposive behaviour occurs:

1) *Where consciousness is apparently normal.*
   'Automatic writing' is an example. Here there is an apparent doubling of direction. The conscious and subconscious actions occur simultaneously and quite independently of each other. The subject writes connectedly and at the same time carries on a conversation or works out a mathematical problem. He is unconscious of the writing.

2) *Where consciousness is a disturbed condition.*
   In many neuroses and in cases of brain injury, subconscious purposive behaviour sometimes takes place while the consciousness is still more or less active. But in such cases it is evident that it is not normal. In hysterical anaesthesia, for instance, a similar 'doubling' occurs as in automatic writing – a manifestation which the investigations of Alfred Binet and Pierre Janet have made generally known.

3) *Where consciousness is absent.*

Subconscious behaviour in its most clearly recognised form occurs when the normal consciousness is apparently entirely obliterated. It has been observed, for instance, during profound unconsciousness, the result of traumatic or pathological lesions in the brain and during certain forms of epilepsy. It occurs during the unconsciousness of normal sleep as somnambulism, and in the somnambulic stage of hypnosis.

In the last two instances, the subconscious behaviour may be said to appear as a result of disturbances of consciousness, and even in the first case, where subconscious behaviour appears in apparently normal men, the psychopathologist holds – and not without reason – that automatism never manifests itself in apparently normal men as other than a syndrome which is the accompaniment of hysteria or other conditions implying a disturbed or diseased state of consciousness.

It is a rule, therefore, that subconscious behaviour is either the result of, or a symptom of, some degree of disorganisation of the normal consciousness. There may be exceptions, but the rule is so general that one would be justified in regarding alleged exceptions with suspicion.

It would lead too far afield to consider all other known types of subconscious behaviour, but I do not think that the description given is inconsistent with the general view that such occurrences as the alteration of personality, insane delusions, 'possessions', and spiritual mediumship are all more or less impure incipient forms of the same psychological process. The subconscious purpose of behaviour under hypnosis agrees with other types in that it appears only during an abnormal state of consciousness.

In its activity, however, hypnotic subconscious behaviour differs considerably from that of all other types. Outside hypnosis, subconscious behaviour is generally very much like conscious behaviour. The mind that contains it reacts in the same way as the conscious mentality does and its attributes do not differ qualitatively or quantitatively from those of the conscious mind.[1] In other words, the behaviour is essentially no different from what it would have been had it been directed by the normal conscious mind.

Here the hypnotic subconscious mentality reveals an apparently supreme dissimilarity. It also uses the same senses that the conscious mind does, but it uses them in a very different manner, and in no less a degree does it differ quantitatively in several of its attributes.

It is particularly in the perfection of 'hypnotic memory' and extreme sense-acuteness that the hypnotic mind is distinguished from the normal conscious mind and from other types of subconscious mentality.

These wonderful attributes were mainly responsible for the creation of the wrong hypothesis and for that sense of the mysterious which overshadowed the work of the first explorers into this condition. Even today it is difficult to look with contempt on those early errors. More systematic knowledge has not rendered these attributes any the less wonderful. They still exert a powerful influence on human imagination, and often thus stand as an impediment between investigation and the attainment of truth.

---

[1] Unless, of course, it is accepted as proved that subconscious mental activity, under certain conditions, possesses the power of direct non-sensorial contacts with other minds embodied or disembodied, or as 'clairvoyant', 'clairaudient', etc.

It must always be borne in mind that the wonder of this hypnotic sense-acuteness and memory is entirely relative to the standard by which they are judged. When judged by the normal conscious mind, they seem to lie outside the order of nature. But when it is realised that this same sense-acuteness and perfection of 'memory' – in a certain sense – constitute the ordinary psychic life of the lower animals, and that even in so high a primate as the chacma the same sense-acuteness is a normal manifestation, then the marvellousness of these attributes becomes less obtrusive.

The great number and sometimes contradictory theories that have been advanced to account for the phenomena of hypnosis need not detain us. The general effect of most hypotheses, whether they be stated in terms purely psychological or purely physiological, is identical. In one particular area there is unanimity in authoritative thought, and that is that hypnosis means a temporary suspension of the cerebral functions. That was the view first advanced by Professor Martin Heidenhain of Breslau, and all later investigation has tended to confirm it.

Now we have seen that it appears to be a general rule that if the functions of the later-developed mental organs are destroyed or inhibited, the functions of the earlier ones can and, under certain circumstances, do become independently active. Functions which have been partially or entirely inhibited by the action of the newer organs can under such circumstances emerge and become dominant in behaviour.

And this is what happens in hypnosis. The functions of the cerebral cortex are suspended and the instinctive mentality with some of its inhibited attributes emerges and becomes visible in behaviour.

Apart from any other proof, the occurrence of the same

behaviour in some form in all organisms from the reptile to the lower primate would have led one to suspect the possibility of its occurrence in man (under favourable conditions and in a degree proportionate to the evolutionary stage his newer mental organs have reached). And proofs are not wanting in hypnotic behaviour itself that the 'subliminal soul' is in reality only the 'animal soul' still present in man's mentality.

One would not expect that in man the separation of mental functions could be brought about in so complete a manner as in lower forms of evolution. In man the development of individual causal memory has reached the zenith. It is in him an evolutionary process of longer duration than in any other existing species, and the newer mental organs are, therefore, far more closely knit than in any other animal.

One would expect that however complete the eclipse of the functions of the higher organs may seem during hypnosis, the subconscious behaviour would still be coloured and influenced by some of them.

And that proves to be so in fact. Yet, when due allowance is made for the influence of causal memory, certain characteristic attributes of the instinctive mentality at once become clearly recognisable in hypnotic behaviour. The chief of these are:

1) Absence of consciousness.

2) Suggestibility. (No trainer of wild animals would fail to recognise this as an especial attribute of the animal mind. By taking advantage of it, man bends to his will the lion and the elephant.)

3) Extreme sense-acuteness.

4) High perfection of the 'place memory'.

The first two characteristics will be self-evident to all students of hypnotism. More detailed attention will, however, have to be devoted to the last two – the general sense-acuteness and the sense of locality – in order to make clear their link with the instinctive mind.

7

Hypnotic Hyperaesthesia

AS THE CAUSAL MEMORY becomes more perfect in the primates, so the senses degenerate. The accumulation of individual memories is quite clearly of far greater value in the animal's struggle against its environment than the acutest senses could ever be. Selection would therefore tend towards the development of the new mentality rather than towards the development of the senses. Degeneration of the senses would keep pace more or less with the evolution of individual causal memory.

In the primates the senses become more perfect the lower one descends in the scale of evolution. In man, sense-degeneration has reached an extreme point. Hypnosis proves, however, that this degeneration in man is not organic, or even functional in the generally accepted sense of the term. The organs are still capable of a very high degree of sensitiveness, and under hypnosis they may actually become functional.

This sensitivity must, therefore, be inhibited by the higher mentality and when this mentality becomes dormant under hypnosis, the inhibition is removed. In the chacma, as one would anticipate, this inhibition has not progressed very far. Its sense-acuteness comes midway between that of normal man on the one hand, and of the higher mammals on the other.

The following record of experimental comparisons between man under hypnosis and the normal chacma will prove how nearly, in respect of the senses, the human hypnotic mentality approximates to that of the normal chacma.

Tactile Sense

Subjects

1) J.B., an 18-year-old Boer girl. Poorly educated but naturally bright and intelligent; neurotic temperament and heredity.

2) Old male chacma; age unknown. Time in captivity unknown, intelligence low; hereditary environmental instincts above average; nervous, vicious and bad-tempered.

During hypnosis the girl was blindfolded and touched on the forehead with the poles of a large steel horseshoe magnet. She was told, "This is the north, and this is the south", as each pole touched her skin. She was thereafter, supposedly, able to distinguish the north and south poles infallibly if touched on the forehead or hands. She could name each pole without a mistake when it was dragged rapidly across the palm of her hand. When the magnet was wrapped in two folds of a thick tablecloth, she could tell the north from the south by lightly touching the extremities of the covered magnet with her finger-tips.

There was some excuse, perhaps, for the original hypothesis that during hypnosis the subject was sensitive to magnetism, and this conviction was strengthened by her own explanation. When the memory of her sensations was fixed by post-hypnotic suggestion, she explained that where the north pole touched her she felt a 'comb of rays' (*kam van strale*) beating into her body to the left, and to the right when the south pole touched her, and that the sensation was the same no matter where on the body she was touched.

Notwithstanding this explanation, a doubt arose as to whether she actually experienced any sensation due purely to the magnetic force. This doubt was created by the fact that her sense of touch, tested in many different ways, proved acute enough to be able to distinguish the two poles without any aid from magnetism.

She was, for instance, tested in the following manner. In her absence, twenty shells of the giant African snail, practically identical in shape, size and weight, were numbered on the inside from one to twenty and placed in that order on a table. The girl, carefully blindfolded, was then brought into the room and allowed to touch the shells, closing her hand over each one in succession without lifting or moving it. She was then taken from the room and in her absence the order of the shells was arbitrarily changed. Brought back still blind-folded, she replaced the shells in their original order, without very much hesitation, and without making a mistake.

It was then found that when a soft-iron or brass horse-shoe was used in place of the steel magnet in the first experiment and it was suggested to her that one extremity was south and the other north, she was able to distinguish them as with the steel magnet and still, post-hypnotically, described her sensations as a 'comb of rays' to the right and left respectively. Further investigation brought to light that the 'comb of rays' was no more than an unintentional suggestion conveyed to her during the experiment. Before she was hypnotised someone had tried to explain magnetism to her and had used the very words 'comb of rays' to describe the parallel lines of the force.

Blindfolded, she was able to distinguish the steel magnet from its soft-iron replica when both were wrapped in several thicknesses of the same cloth by touching the two extremities with her finger-tips.

The chacma was taught to associate the presence of the steel magnet with an imitation snake of which he was afraid. Both snake and magnet were hidden in a bag of thick cloth.[1]

---

[1] This experiment was arranged before it was discovered that magnetism had no share in the sensation experienced by the hypnotised girl.

An identical bag contained a soft-iron replica of the steel magnet and was associated with the presence of a plantain at the bottom. A bag was always so placed that in order to ascertain whether it contained the snake or the plantain the chacma had to draw it towards him and was compelled to touch through the cloth either the magnet or the soft-iron imitation. As soon as the memory was fixed in his mind, he never once made a mistake. The slightest touch was sufficient to indicate to him whether the bag contained the magnet or the replica.

Taste

Subjects

1) J.B. (as above).

2) Male chacma about three years old. Bred in captivity; artificially reared; very high intelligence.

As a baby, the chacma had developed the habit of sucking its thumb. The thumb became raw and painful and all the means commonly resorted to in the case of human babies failed to cure it of the habit. Eventually the lady who had charge of it placed on the thumb a glove finger saturated in quinine. As the chacma grew up, it retained a deep and perhaps not unnatural aversion to quinine. After some preparatory instructive experiments it was found that this baboon could in darkness – to exclude the possibility of visual identification – detect by taste the presence of sulphate of quinine in a solution of one milligram in four litres of water.

Another chacma who had once accidentally eaten a poison fruit could detect by taste similarly infinitesimal quantities of the juice in water or fruit.

The hypnotised girl, without any instructive preparation, could detect the drug in the same solution as the chacma. If there was any difference in threshold value, it seemed slightly lower in the girl than in the chacma. The weakest solution used in either case was one mg to four litres, and the chacma appeared occasionally to be in doubt, and there was reason to believe that he sometimes had to taste the liquid two or three times before he was quite sure. The girl was never in doubt. It was only necessary for her to place a single drop on her tongue and the moment she closed her mouth she knew whether the liquid contained quinine or not.

The same chacma could in strong light detect the presence of the drug in a slightly weaker solution – equal to 1 in 800,000 of water. The hypnotised girl showed doubt and hesitation and her errors amounted to 40 per cent. When the strength of the solution was raised to 1 in 600,000, she became infallible. When not hypnotised, she could detect the quinine only in a solution four times the above strength.

Sight

In distant vision the superiority of the chacma seemed greater still. A young captive male could at a distance of six miles, over a landscape flickering with mirage, recognise without fail among a group of people a human friend to whom he was greatly attached. At that distance in such atmospheric conditions no normal human, even with a good pair of binoculars, could distinguish human beings from cattle.

Our observation of wild troops convinced me that even this perhaps does not represent the limit of chacma vision. Among hunters the chacma has the reputation of being the most far-sighted of wild animals living in Africa.

The hypnotised girl at just half that distance failed to recognise an acquaintance, and approached infallibility only with a good pair of binoculars, though this would, in her normal state, have been impossible.

Smell

Subjects

1) M.B., a 21-year-old Boer girl. Fairly well educated; sister to J.B. (above); neurotic.

2) Several male and female chacmas.

Twenty different people, the majority unknown to the girl, each handled a different small object and then placed it in a receptacle. The girl, blindfolded, took out one object after another, and by smelling the object and the hands of the different people handed each object back to the person who had handled it first without a mistake. By smell she could identify any number of acquaintances sitting in a room, walking past each one at a distance of one yard and sniffing the air.

Still blindfolded, she could find a grain of musk hidden anywhere in a room. When a small fragment of *asafoetida* tied to a thread was dragged over a table in an irregular course, half an hour later she could trace out its path by holding her blindfolded face a few inches from the surface of the table.

Investigations with a number of chacmas made it apparent that although their sense of smell is far inferior to that of many species of mammals, and considerably below that of the hypnotised girl, it is, nevertheless, greatly superior to that of the average normal human being. A blindfolded chacma could not recognise an acquaintance standing within a yard.

But when the baboon could touch the person, it invariably made use of the sense of smell to aid it in determining identity. Its nose would be thrust up against the clothes of the person examined and it often seemed as if there was considerable hesitation and doubt. A full-grown male was unable to trace the course of as strongly scented a fruit as a pineapple after it had been dragged along the ground, and was unaware of its presence when it was hidden in a bag three yards away.

Hearing

Subjects

1) M.B. (as above).

2) Several captive chacmas.

Of a number of experiments which definitely established the superiority of hearing in the hypnotised girl I will describe only the following.

A sound of constant volume imitating the hiss of a snake, and in the case of the chacmas associated with the presence of an imitation rubber snake, could be clearly heard by the hypnotised girl at a distance of 230 yards. The distance at which average normal human beings could hear the sound lay between 20 and 30 yards. The chacmas could hear it at a distance of between 50 and 65 yards.[1]

The difficulty of arriving at anything like an exact comparison between the respective threshold values of these stimuli will be appreciated, but where we are dealing with values so

---

[1] [It is unfortunate that Marais did not make precise comparisons in all the experiments between the same subject's sensitivity under hypnosis and in a normal state. Further experiments should be conducted. His central point of enhanced sensitivity seems, however, fairly made. – R.A.]

inconceivably low when judged by a normal human standard, I do not think that a very exact comparison is necessary in order to prove at least a convincing correspondence – or the reverse.

And that this correspondence does exist it is hardly possible to doubt. It will be seen that in two senses, hearing and sight, there seems to be a considerable deference, but, taken generally, there is undoubtedly a closer agreement between the hypnotised human being and the chacma than between the hypnotised and normal human beings.

And it seems to me a fair presumption that if hypnosis could be induced in the chacma and its behaviour in that condition controlled and directed, it would be found that its hypnotic sense-acuteness approximated that of many of the lower mammals.

8

The Sense of Locality, Hypnotic and Normal

THE SEQUENCE 'memory' of the hypnotic mentality is another outstanding feature which distinguishes it from all normal human psychic processes, and which has done much to invest the state with that glamour of mysticism which darkened the pathway of the early explorers.

It will be remembered that in the last chapter an experiment was described in which a hypnotised girl recalled the sequence of twenty practically identical shells, and that the order of the sequence was instantaneously conveyed to her through the sense of touch alone. This does not represent an ultimate feat of the hypnotic 'memory'; longer sequences can be remembered with the same spontaneity and quickness, and there is always the same ease of 'recall'. Nor does it generally make any difference through which sense organ the stimulus is conveyed. A lengthy and arbitrary series can be registered just as effectively through hearing, sight, taste or smell as through the tactile sense.

The use of the word 'memory' must not be taken as an implication of the hypothesis that these two faculties are in any sense identical. It will be seen that, whatever else the 'sequence memory' may be, it certainly is not 'memory' as the term is understood in the human sense. Under hypnosis it is, like all other hypnotic faculties, to a certain extent influenced and coloured by the slumbering consciousness, and under these conditions there is a suggestive resemblance to normal memory. It achieves results compassed by normal memory, as wine resembles water. And there the similarity ends. The means adopted by the hypnotic memory to attain these results – the methods of its reaction – differ as widely from those of ordinary memory as any two other psychic processes can differ.

The comparative investigation of 'sequence memory' behaviour makes it clear that this particular hypnotic psychological process is identical with the *sense of locality*, and this sense of locality, in its purest manifestation in lower animals, is neither identical with the causal memory, nor even related to it.

In fact, the two faculties invariably appear in the same species in an inverse ratio: the higher the causal memory, the more deficient is the sense of locality. Its highest manifestation occurs in the so-called 'homing instinct' common to most living beings, and no one who has devoted any attention to the behaviour of butterflies, for instance, will have failed to notice the perfection of the sense of locality in a mentality devoid of any trace of individual causal memory.

The nature of the sense of locality and its occurrence in higher forms will be rendered more intelligible by a systematic record of behaviour. For this purpose, I shall describe the behaviour of an animal with very deficient individual causal memory (taking the chacma as a comparative standard) and compare its sense of locality with that of normal man, possessing the most perfect causal memory; and lastly I shall give an experimental record showing the operation of the sense of locality in man under hypnosis.

Deficient Causal Memory

A mare of average intelligence which we had an opportunity of observing gave birth to a foal. Two days after birth, the foal was accidentally drowned. The mother was present, witnessed the drowning, the recovery of the dead body and the burying. Throughout these proceedings she showed great distress, and when the body was recovered she nuzzled it repeatedly, softly whinnying. After she had stood by and witnessed the burying, she commenced at once running about wildly, whinnying for the foal. She returned twice to the scene of the drowning but never to the grave. Her excited and distressed search continued for eight days. It was quite clear that only the maternal sense directed her behaviour. There was not apparent the least memory that she had seen her foal put underground.

Compare this with the behaviour of a chacma under very similar circumstances. A tame female in captivity gave birth and when the baby was a few weeks old it was severely injured in an accident. As its life was in danger it was forcibly removed from the mother, with the object of relieving its suffering and, if possible, saving its life.

She showed even deeper distress at the parting than the mare had done. For three days she hardly ate at all, and kept calling, night and day. Whenever she caught sight of the person who had taken the baby from her, she showed intense excitement.

On the third day the baby died, despite treatment. The dead body was placed on the ground before the mother. Her restless excitement at once subsided. She approached the body, making the chacma sounds of endearment, and touched it twice with her hands. She then put her face close to the back of the dead infant, touching its skin with her mouth, at the same time moving her lips in the usual chacma manner. Immediately afterwards she got up, uttered a succession of cries, walked to a corner and sat down quietly in the sun, apparently taking no more interest in the body. Half an hour later it was removed. She still showed no interest. She allowed the body to be taken up and when it was held under her very nose she showed no response. From the moment the dead body was shown to her, all her restless movements ended. She ceased calling, took an interest in her surroundings, and again began behaving in the normal chacma manner.

It will be seen that in the behaviour of the chacma mother, there was immediate reaction to a very complex causal memory. It seems to imply a comprehension of the significance of death and its consequence. In the mare, there was no apparent causal recollection of so simple a fact as the final disappearance of the foal underground.

We will now see what the sense of locality is like in a mentality so deficient in forming the simplest causal memory.

This same mare was taken through a pathless tract of *bushveld* on a five day journey. With her were a number of old hunters all possessing a high sense of locality, as this is reckoned among men. They steered their course by the sun chiefly. At their destination – the banks of the Limpopo – they travelled up and down the river for long distances and remained there almost two weeks.

In the meantime heavy rain had fallen, destroying every vestige of spoor. They started back from a spot about twenty miles lower down the river than where they had first reached it on their northward journey. It was their intention to travel by as straight a course as possible to their original starting-point.

It is a 'bad' tract of country, and to get lost in it is a matter of very little difficulty. Numbers of experienced hunters have had to bear witness to its dangers. Several have left their bones to bleach on its waterless sands. It is quite pathless, quite flat and thickly covered with bush and trees – an endless repetition of the same vistas. There are no outstanding landmarks anywhere, and one can never see farther ahead than a few yards.

The mare, carrying a pack and unattended, led the party. On the afternoon of the first day of their return journey she turned slightly out of her course and suddenly stopped. On coming up with her the men found, to their surprise, that the spot was their last camping place on the northward journey. They had been until then under the impression that they were a long distance east of their route.

The mare continued unerringly and stopped at each camping place. To the experienced hunters who followed her as they would have followed an infallible guide, it seemed nothing short of miraculous. If there had been any vestige of the spoor the thing was explainable, but after the heavy rains and the long time that had elapsed, it is highly improbable that there was any scent, and there certainly were no tracks to guide her.

But even if there had been a spoor and scent on their original route, how could one account for her reaching the last camping place? She had steered her course to it, as with a compass, through country she had never seen before and in a direction she had certainly never travelled. And this was the same mare which could not remember that she had seen her foal put underground!

The sense of locality is therefore clearly not an attribute nor even an accompaniment of the causal memory. It is quite evidently a function of the instinctive soul, and the lower one descends in the scale of evolution, the more perfect it becomes. A bird bred and hatched in a certain locality, without any experience, travels across the world and in a year's time finds its way back infallibly to the very tree in the forest whence it started.

Perfect Causal Memory

It can be experimentally proved that this sense of locality is more deficient in man than in any primate, and more deficient in cultured than in primitive man. It is far less active in the lower primates than in the higher mammals, and apparently more perfect in the birds than in the mammals. It is, therefore, as far as man is concerned, an anciently submerged psychic attribute, and so atrophied through disuse in cultured man, so completely inhibited by conscious memory, that its very existence is hard to detect. But it is still there, and can be efficiently functional under hypnosis, as the following experimental investigation will show.

A nest of a small species of Namaqua partride (*Pterocles*) was found on the Springbok Flats and its position indicated by three inconspicuous marks, all at long distances from the nest. Anyone knowing the marks, and with the assistance of a signaller, could find the nest. Without these aids it seemed humanly impossible ever to discover the nest again after one had gone any distance away from it. The country is so absolutely level that it can hardly be said to possess a watershed. It is in addition quite trackless, without a single conspicuous natural feature, and is covered with shrubs and grass, all monotonously unvarying.

Three eggs had been hatched just after the nest was found. The female bird was on different occasions disturbed at the nest. She invariably flew straight away at great speed until she vanished in the distance. The direction in which she flew was determined by the side on which the nest was approached. It seemed impossible that she could ever find the nest again by any of the ordinary psychic processes that a human being employs. Generally within half an hour she returned, flying swiftly and in an apparently straight line to the nest.

After the duration of her absences had been ascertained, she was trapped and temporarily blinded. She was then taken a distance of three hundred paces from the nest, liberated, and watched for about two hours. During this time she kept calling at intervals and made three short flights, but not once in the direction of the nest. She was then caught and taken a distance of seven miles to a settlement where she could not have been before. Here, her sight was restored and she was liberated. She flew straight back to the nest.

A number of different men and boys all long resident on the Flats and experienced hunters were then tested in the following manner.

Each one was taken to the nest and allowed to study the surroundings for as long and as carefully as he liked. He was then taken in a straight line away from the nest a distance of two hundred yards and again at right angles to this line for another hundred yards. He was then told to find the nest.

Out of five individuals thus tested, not one even came near the place. One, after wandering for some time – he admitted becoming gradually more confused – struck his own original spoor and so found his starting-point. But it was quite evident that not one could have found the nest by his sense of locality alone.

A boy of fourteen, born on the Flats and known to possess a high sense of locality, was then tested in the same manner. In three trials he never succeeded in getting near the correct locality. He was then hypnotised at the nest and led a long distance away while every device was adopted to obliterate his sense of direction.

About a mile from the nest he was stopped and told to go back.

He unhesitatingly did so in a perfectly straight line. It was ascertained that his ability to find the nest was not in any way affected by the distance he was taken away, nor by the nature of the route. Even where a series of circles were described, and numberless zigzags and angled courses, he was never in the least doubt as to the exact direction in which the nest lay. When he was led away blind-folded and the same methods of mystification were adopted, the moment his eyes were opened, he invariably turned and walked in the right direction.

If, however, he was led away blindfolded even a short distance and told to find the nest still blindfolded, he not only could not do it, but as often as not walked directly away from it. And the same result followed if he was led away open-eyed for a short distance and then told to go back blindfolded.

It is evident, therefore, that in the hypnotised boy qualitatively the same incomprehensible faculty of location became functional under hypnosis as existed in the mother bird.

Another interesting fact that became apparent was the evident influence which sight exercises on the operation of the faculty. Trained pigeons if temporarily blinded cannot 'home'. They can find their way back on fairly dark nights, but if the night is very dark they become confused and lose their sense of direction.

But the sense of locality is certainly not just a mere 'matter of seeing'. It will be remembered that in the cases mentioned the subject 'homed' in a direction which led through localities never before seen. The homing pigeon does this habitually. It is usually placed in a basket and carried inside a closed vehicle for great distances and returns by a direct route. Under such conditions there can be no 'sight memory' to guide it.

An explanation that suggests itself is this: Every movement through space, every turning of the body on its axis, is registered in the 'subconscious' mentality. So that the animal at the end of the journey, even when it has been shut up in a box, bears within itself a complete psychic chart of the route traversed.

But while initially this seems the only reasonable psychological theory, there are difficulties in the way. It cannot account for homing by a route different to one traversed. In the case of the boy mentioned in *Chapter 3*, for instance, it is difficult to imagine how a complete psychic chart of a single line could confer all the benefits of a mathematically accurate geographic map.

Further research will, no doubt, make clear a great deal that at present seems inexplicable in the sense of locality. In the present state of knowledge – if one is searching for marvels – it must always seem that this faculty of the instinctive soul is just as wonderful as any of the alleged exploits of telepathy and clairvoyance. An animal possessing it must indeed be both clairvoyant and telepathic.

Compared with normal human mental powers, it seems to border on the miraculous. It is equivalent to the attainment of knowledge through no known sense organ. Its manifestations seem to justify the conclusion that there must exist a method of communication between mind and the external world other than through the channels recognised by normal men.

To recapitulate briefly: the sense of locality in its most perfect form is invariably associated with the mentality in which the individual causal memory is least developed.

The mare could not remember the simplest cause and effect, and yet could steer her course unerringly through quite unknown country; while man, an animal possessing the highest causal memory, was not only unable to imitate this achievement, but failed to understand the psychic process involved.

And an investigation of the phenomena of hypnotism justifies the conclusion that the hypnotic memory is no other than the phyletic sense of locality, particularly and temporarily liberated from the inhibiting control of the functions associated with the cerebral cortex.

This inhibition of instinctive faculties, which we have already considered in the chacma, is therefore apparently a process inevitably associated with the development of the new mentality, and an examination of its occurrence in man renders more intelligible the nature of its beginnings in the lower primates.

9
Specific Consequences of
the Evolution of Primate Mentality

THIS SOMEWHAT lengthy digression will have made it clear that the evolution of the mind of individual memory and the consequent submergence of the mind of hereditary memory is a process discernible in the highest primate, man, as well as in that comparatively lower primate, the chacma.

The vast and fundamental difference which exists between the old mind and the new in its method of reaction to the environment has had, as may be imagined, certain far-reaching consequences; and the chacma, whose behaviour is directed chiefly by the new mentality, seems to exhibit these consequences in no uncertain manner. Some consideration of these effects is necessary.

The evolution of instinctive mentality is always in the direction of more complete specialisation. The higher and more complex an hereditary instinct is, the more efficiently does it react under certain definite natural conditions – namely, the conditions that selected it – and the less able it is to direct behaviour beneficially under changed conditions or new ones.

Whenever an animal adapts itself suddenly to changed conditions, it will be found that this is not a reaction of the phyletic memory, but is invariably due to its inhibition, partial or complete, by the acquisition of individual causal memory. The animal adapts itself not by *means* of the instinct, but *in spite* of it.

Heredity of behaviour is one of the distinguishing marks of the phyletic mind. An instinct is sometimes so complex and its beneficial reaction dependent upon such a long chain of causes and effects that the essential difference between 'instinct' and 'intelligence' is easily missed.

Many careful and distinguished observers have regarded these complex instincts as a complete vindication of the contention that such behaviour is directed by 'intelligence'. If the memory which directs behaviour is hereditary, it is quite certainly instinctive. An individually acquired environmental causal memory is never transmitted from parents to offspring.

And because an instinct is in itself unchangeable, except through the long and dangerously destructive process of natural selection, its possession always entails a disadvantageous limitation of the existence-scope of the organism whose behaviour it controls.

It is here that the evolution of the new mind becomes apparent, working towards the breaking down of disadvantageous limitation. It is the great psychic generalising process of natural selection.

By the acquisition of individual memories, an organism is to a proportionate extent freed from the stringent necessity of limiting its activities to a defined environment. But even with this new weapon in its armoury, the struggle of a species against nature is still hampered by the existence of hereditary behaviour.

Its tendency is always to neutralise the beneficial action of individual memory. Selection therefore gradually renders inoperative the mind which determines hereditary behaviour. As one ascends in the evolutionary scale through the primates, the mind of hereditary memory becomes more and more inactive. Most of its attributes, although still in existence as the functions of existing brain centres, are inhibited by the new mentality from taking any share in the direction of behaviour.

Some of these instinctive attributes which are still beneficial, and therefore necessary, seem to be controlled by the new mind. Their reaction can in different degrees be either inhibited or called into action voluntarily. This is so, as will be seen, in the higher primates even in the case of so universal and essential an instinct as the sexual sense. Under such conditions an instinct, even when operative, loses its stereotyped character, that fixed and changeless response to outward stimulation which is the outstanding characteristic of activity in the purely instinctive soul.

The power which causal memory confers of immediate adaptation to changed environmental conditions affords a species an enhanced protection against the hostility of nature generally, and this has a remarkable result. The elements in nature hostile to organic life – and that seems to be all nature – constitute the means by which natural selection operates.

Natural selection is in effect the elimination of the not sufficiently specialised. When, therefore, an organism is protected against this active hostility, it is to the same extent protected against natural selection. It is something in the nature of a vicious circle: natural selection in the end destroying itself.

It will be seen presently that this protection can hardly be regarded, from the point of view of well-being of the species, as a beneficial process. Our present knowledge of nature precludes the concept of any other force which could make for the endurance of organic beings, and we are, therefore, apparently face to face with the inevitable conclusion that a condition disadvantageous to a species has been attained by natural selection. At first glance it seems a contradiction in terms. The very fundamental conception of selection is the retention of beneficial attributes only. A disadvantageous condition cannot be brought about by natural selection.

This apparent paradox is not a real one. It is based on a confusion of ideas, and practical experience of nature soon teaches one to distinguish between a *primary benefit* and a *secondary accidental disadvantage* resulting from it. As long as the accidental disadvantage does not completely outweigh the main advantage, it will continue as a satellite attendant upon its primary. Such an accidental disadvantageous result is the protection from natural selection in the chacma. The primary advantage clearly was the removal of environmental limitation, and this removal was brought about by a process destructive of natural selection itself.

The difficulty of understanding such a simple and universal law is increased when the mind is influenced by that trend of abstract speculation which is apt to regard evolution by means of natural selection as some infallible process tending towards some ideal state of perfection.

A direct and practical knowledge of nature soon corrects this wrong idea, and renders comprehensible how such an apparently disadvantageous condition as protection from selection could have been brought about in a species.

It becomes at once evident that in the whole scheme of organic evolution, no 'perfection' has ever been attained and that in the nature of things, it is unattainable.

The end of natural selection is specialisation, and every specialisation is at once followed by a number of disadvantages which may increase in valence in proportion to the progress of the specialisation, until they neutralise entirely the benefit which it originally conferred.

The specialisation then becomes selectively modified, and this modification means only specialisation in a new direction. The process, therefore, is an unending one, and the attainment of perfection – that is, an organism in perfect accord with its environment – is a practical impossibility. Natural selection regularly brings about accidental and often disadvantageous consequences, and the reduction of the power of natural selection by the acquisition of non-hereditary environmental memories is an example.

*

This enlargement from the confining tendencies of the instinctive mind was the immediate benefit conferred upon the chacma by the attainment of a dominant individual causal memory.

We have seen how it has enabled the species to penetrate the most varied natural environments. They have indeed become citizens of a large world. For them, restriction to a locality no longer exists. For them, there is no longer a supreme danger in the invasion of threatening competition or any sudden or radical change in natural conditions. A door of escape is always open to them. They can either adapt themselves instantly to the new conditions or migrate, even where such migration entails a new environment.

The psychic power of immediate adaptation, by the acquisition of and reaction to individual causal memories, culminates in man, the highest primate. His exalted development of the new mentality has rendered the species heir to all the earth and the fullness thereof.

Against his invasion neither the sub-tropical deserts nor the polar ice has been proof. But if this was the benefit which causal memory conferred upon the chacma, then the indirect accidental result of that evolutionary process – namely, the protection against stringent natural selection – has had results in other directions which, one is inclined to believe, must eventually have a profound effect upon the fate of any species.

Whenever a species is protected from the severity of natural selection, certain definite results ensue, and these are always proportionate to the extent and duration of the protection. These changes are included under the general and somewhat meaningless term 'degeneration', and they are, of course, especially noticeable in man and in domestic animals, where natural selection is at its lowest ebb.

When these changes are compared, it is found that two of them seem to assume prime importance. These are

1) divergence from specific type, and

2) disturbances of the sexual sense.

On examination, it appears that the real cause of their apparent importance is due to two factors:

1) They represent the sum of a great number of changes which affect every organ and the function of every organ; and

2) the fate of the species seems to be so deeply involved in them.

It is to these two changes, as they relate to the chacma, that the next two chapters will be devoted.

10
Divergence From Type

'TYPE' MAY BE DEFINED as the mean of the hereditary beneficial attributes established by natural selection in a species. Variation from type is a thing of constant and regular occurrence. Nature, in the popular saying, never produces two things exactly alike.

It will be found, however, that variation in any species, if it can be measured at all, generally exhibits a regular curve.

The Dutch botanist Hugo de Vries found, for instance, in measuring the length of a number of seed pods, that the majority of pods fell under the numbers nearest the mean. The absolute mean contained the greatest number, and as the extremes were approached they became regularly less – on the one side the long ones, and on the other the short. And this law holds good throughout nature. It is, in fact, no more than a mathematical demonstration of the concrete truth upon which rests our abstract conception of 'type'.

Theoretically, one would assume that the tendency of natural selection would be continually to eliminate the more extreme variants. Individuals possessing in the most perfect form the selected characteristics would be the ones most likely to survive, and these would be typical individuals.

This theoretical interpretation of the method of selection has also been empirically verified. The American naturalist Hermon Bumpus found, on measuring birds of one species that had been injured during a storm, that the individuals that perished were the extreme variants. Those that recovered were the individuals nearest the mean. Weldon and Tower found that the same thing occurred in beetles and terrestrial molluscs. Nor could it well be otherwise. If the death rate was not highest among the variants, the theory of natural selection could not stand.

It is, of course, conceivable that variations may sometimes under favourable conditions, prove more beneficial than the typical attributes, and it is possible that such discontinuous variations or mutations may, as Hugo de Vries assumes, occur at long intervals, and that these may be the origin of distinct varieties and species.

Whether this be so or not, it seems certain that favourable variations are the exception in nature. *The general rule is that divergence from type is the mark of the unfit.*

In this country, instances of extreme variation among the larger mammals occur very rarely, but they are not unknown. In such cases, it would seem, sexual selection tends to become the dominant factor in the elimination.

Albinism is an instance of such extreme variation. Several naturalists have noted that albino birds, kept under observation, did not succeed in finding mates, and we have trustworthy records of the same thing being observed among the larger African mammals.

Thus an albino springbok (*Antidorcas marsupialis marsupialis*) was solitary, and whenever she came in contact with a troop of her own kind, she was mercilessly attacked by male and female alike.

A white klipspringer (*Oreotragus saltator*) was also so continually persecuted by other klipspringers that it took shelter near a homestead and became quite tame. It was never seen with a mate.

A black wildebeest (*Connochaetes gnou*) with a white blaze[1] was also thrust out of the herd, which it always followed at a safe distance.

A fur-horned kudu (*Strepciceros*) was solitary, but this may have been due to the continual pursuit of hunters who were anxious to secure so unusual a trophy.

It would thus seem as if natural selection had two strings to her bow in the maintenance of type:

1) A greater incidence of mortality among ordinary variants is the general method; and

2) with extra forms there is usually protective sexual exclusion.

What would be the effect on the type of a species if it was partially protected from natural selection? It is self-evident that in such circumstances any variant, whether it was a progressive modification or a reversion to ancient type, would have a chance of existence more nearly equal to that of the typical individual than it would under conditions of severe selection.

The atavistic revenant and the progressive variant would be protected against the hostile conditions that would otherwise make their destruction certain. The variation curve would become irregular. It would no longer be the same as under the more usual natural conditions. The members of the species falling within the absolute mean would become relatively less, and a portion of the individuals that would fall out of the average in a species subject to selection would now have a tendency to be distributed progressively towards the ends of the curve. Under protection, therefore, variation would tend to have an increasing influence on type.

---

[1] A not uncommon variant. It is beyond doubt a reversion.

That this is so among such highly protected species as the domestic animals is quite evident. If we take one of the latest additions to the category, the African guinea-fowl, where a comparatively short period in protection has created the common domestic tendency towards albinism, it will be found that there is no selective tendency adverse to the patchy individuals, other than that brought about by man's intervention.

It is interesting to note the effect of variation on hereditary type in this species. If a number of domestic birds are allowed to mix with wild birds under natural conditions, white marks and patches will appear for perhaps three or four generations. Then they entirely disappear.[1]

If, on the other hand, they are mixed with wild birds in captivity, or recently tamed ones, the hereditary effects on type are far more lasting. I know of cases where a very slight admixture of domestic blood has caused the persistence of white patches for twenty years after its introduction. It is hardly possible to doubt that in the wild flock the variation is eliminated by natural selection, and that it continues in the protected flock because of the weakening of selection.

One would anticipate that the chacma, just to the extent that it is protected by its 'intelligence' from the more rigorous natural selection, would show a tendency towards the same variation that is conspicuous in man and the domestic animals. And such anticipation would be verified by a very little observation.

When we commenced our investigation we had not such anticipation, and yet one of the first impressions we formed was that there was something very much wrong with the 'type' of the chacma.

---

[1] Crossing under natural conditions is unsuccessful if care is not taken to exclude extreme variants. Extreme forms have a tendency to separate from the wild birds.

It was possible in a comparatively short time to learn to know and to recognise individuals in a large troop, and this was contrary to all our experience with gregarious mammals outside the order of the primates. It took perhaps a little more time and a little closer study than would be necessary to know and to distinguish the same number of individuals among an unfamiliar human race, but I do not think that the closest study or unlimited time would enable one to attain a similar result with the same number of springboks, for instance.

The first explanation that suggested itself was this: that, since the chacma, after all, more closely resembles the human being than any non-primate mammal, an eye trained to know and to recognise human individuals would discriminate more easily in this closely related species than in a more distant one. But more exact methods of observation soon convinced us that the ultimate reason lay in the fact that there was a greater and more extreme individual divergence from type in the chacma than in any 'natural' non-primate species known to us.

There was a greater difficulty when one approached the question of definition. What exactly *was* this variation?

It was at once apparent that certain conspicuous modifications had a tendency to recur constantly, and it was perhaps possible to ascertain the extent and the percentage of their occurrence. But these outstanding 'single' modifications did not lie at the root of the matter. It was rather the sum of an infinite number of small variations in each individual that rendered recognition easy.

We ascertained the existence of certain distinct correlations, such as, for instance, the shape and size of the occipital ridge to the relative length of arm. Exhaustive research would no doubt prove that such correlations of growth are attendant upon every somatic modification, great or small. But generally our own attempts at systematising yielded negative results, and gradually the conviction was forced on us that variation in the chacma is so irregular as to defy definition and to baffle all effort at classification.

I think just the same difficulty would be experienced, to an enhanced degree, in attempting to classify or define divergence from type in man. It is possible that all these variations may occur in accordance with the Mendelian laws of heredity, but even this we were unable to ascertain either experimentally, or by observation under natural conditions.

Though one thing seems certain: this variation is of the same nature as that occurring in man and the domestic animals. These species are, of course, far more completely protected from natural selection than the chacma, and the tendency in them is therefore far more advanced.

In man, the most highly protected of mammals, individual divergence from type has reached an extreme point. No single organ or function of his body is exempt; even the vital organs show a degree of variation for which identical conditions in nature will be sought in vain.

It seems, therefore, a safe assumption that the tendency to vary in the primates must be progressive, and that the rate of progress is determined by mental development, even if most of the modifications are in the nature of acquired characteristics created by the environment only, and are therefore not transmissible. Some in each generation would be hereditary and must have an increasingly adverse influence on the maintenance of type.

Psychologically, the same extraordinary divergence is apparent in the chacma. Reference has been made to the difference between the vervet monkey and the chacma as far as hereditary individual memory is concerned, and the fact was noted that in the chacma there was considerable variation in the inheritance of phyletic memory, which in the lower species was quite uniform.

This psychological variation, like somatic divergence, seems to be reducible to a more or less regular curve. At the one extremity come the individuals with highly developed phyletic knowledge and proportionately undeveloped reasoning powers. Their mind is instinctive, their reasoning 'animal-like'. The casual observer might describe them as 'stupid'.

In the middle comes the common type, in which the two souls are equally developed. These individuals inherit a certain amount of hereditary memory – less than the lower type does, but still certainly directive – and their individual causal memory is also 'average'.

At the other extreme come the highly intelligent animals – the clever ones – who are nearly devoid of hereditary memory. And between these three types come the usual gradations.

One would, on anthropomorphic grounds, be inclined to assume that the highly intelligent type of mentality would be the one most likely to be beneficial to the species in the struggle to live, and that this must therefore be the one towards which natural selection tends. It would appear, however, that as far as the chacma is concerned, both the 'animal' soul on the one hand and the more human-like soul on the other are, under existing conditions, in the nature of less advantageous variants.

The mentality combining both types more or less equally is clearly the one which has thus far proved most beneficial to the species. But it is quite conceivable that environmental conditions might arise under which the higher mentality would be selected and a new variety or species thus created.

That is a conception more in accord with our present knowledge of evolution than the popular erroneous conclusion that natural selection must necessarily be working towards the establishment of 'human' mentality in all primates.

There would be just as much reason for assuming that the long-necked okapi (*Okapi johnstoni*) must necessarily in time become a giraffe.

One can hardly fail to notice the analogy which exists between the psychological variation curve of the chacma and that of man. Human mental variation has at the one extreme congenital idiocy and all the grades of 'weak-mindedness' up to the average intelligence. On the other side come the mental prodigies, the artists, the poets, the geniuses and, finally, the insane. These extreme variants seem to be representative of the same phyletic types of mentality that are conspicuous in the chacma.

It would seem that in the chacma mental variation is very closely correlated to the general shape of the skull. The two extreme cranial types are:

a) one end of the scale, the pronounced cynocephalic form with excessive orbital ridges, a greatly developed occipital ridge and an extreme orbital structure[1]; and

b) at the other, the 'round-headed' type in which these characteristics are much less developed, and the general shape of the skull tends towards that of the anthropoid.

Needless to say, the more human-like mentality is invariably associated with the more anthropoidal cranium, and the animal-like with the cynocephalic.

---

[1] The 'gorilla' ridge and the orbital ridges are of course invariably correlated, as one would anticipate from their structural connection.

It is interesting to note that this cranial variation of the chacma is 'recapitulated' in ontogenetic development, and from the nature of the development of the individual one would infer that the chacma is descended from an ancestral form which far more closely resembled the existing anthropoids and which may have possessed a higher mentality than the existing type. The chacma foetus and a newborn baby are far more chimpanzee-like than the adult is. Indeed, at certain stages of development the foetus resembles the adult chimpanzee more closely than the adult chacma. Even the first hair is quite black and resembles that of the chimpanzee in growth and texture. If a series of skulls, from foetal to full maturity, are compared it will be seen at once how the cynocephalic characteristics increase with age, and what a great difference there is in this respect between the foetal skull and that of the adult.[1]

It is, I think, the persistence of the anthropomorphic type of skull during youth which has given rise to the popular idea in South Africa that there are two species of baboons – long-faced and short-faced – and that the short-faced are always 'cleverer'.

[1] The individual development of the chimpanzee is analogous. The foetus is much more human-like than the adult. Here there is reason for believing that this anthropoid also represents a 'degenerate' type – that is to say, it is descended from ancestors which were more human-like than the adult chimpanzees. As in the chacma, the resemblance persists in the early post-natal stage of development, when it is also very noticeable in behaviour. The chimpanzee baby cries so like a human baby that the sounds are easily mistakable. It 'pulls faces' in the same way and similarly jerks its arms and legs spasmodically. At a little later stage of development it shows acute distress by the human method of throwing itself on the ground, aimlessly kicking with its legs and moving its arms about. The eyes are tight shut, the face is distorted and its wailing cries are very like those of a human child at a lower stage of individual development.

[Contemporary theories of the Dutch ethologist Adriaan Kortlandt (though not as yet widely accepted) suggest, as did Marais, that the ancestor of the chimpanzee was more human-like than is the chimpanzee itself. – R.A.]

The short-faced variation certainly does occur in adult forms, and, as I have suggested, it is associated with a higher type of mentality, but it does not occur to such an extent in mature individuals that it should suggest the idea of two distinct varieties.

I think the only explanation is that young ones are mistaken for individuals of a distinct variety and the occurrence of an occasional adult 'short-face' serves to strengthen the impression. There are better grounds for believing that occasionally either the long-faced or short-faced variation has shown a tendency to become predominant in certain isolated troops; our own observation, however, afforded no evidence at first hand of the existence of such a tendency, and I think second-hand evidence in its favour should not be accepted without reserve.

On even more dependable evidence rests the assertion that many years ago in an isolated troop in Rooiberg the tendency to albinism appeared as a hereditary characteristic. We saw a white female that was said to have been captured from this troop as a baby. A trustworthy informant, a Wesleyan missionary who had been stationed for many years in this country, informed us that at one time he estimated that ten per cent of the individuals in the troop showed white bands and patches. Pure white ones were rare.

If the characteristics were really hereditary and not due to the conditions of the environment or to something in the nature of an infectious disease, the circumstance would be extremely interesting, pointing to the origin of a genuine mutation. What makes it doubtful is the fact that although true albinism is quite common among natives, its heredity in the human being is highly questionable.

One would anticipate that the anthropoids, possessing as they do a far higher protective mentality, would exhibit generally greater individual divergence from type than the chacma; and our present somewhat scanty knowledge of the great manlike apes seems to confirm this assumption.[1]

My own knowledge of the chacma leads me to believe that some of the different forms of the chimpanzee which have in recent years been discovered in this country and which have been assigned to distinct varieties will eventually be found to be continuous variants of the same species. Even now it is becoming difficult to draw a hard-and-fast line between two such widely different forms as the gorilla and the chimpanzee. Several specimens of gorilla-like chimpanzees and chimpanzee-like gorillas have been secured which point to the probability that those two forms are connected by an unbroken chain of intermediate types.

It is possible, as I have pointed out in the case of the chacma, that there may be a strong tendency in the higher primates for certain variations to become predominant in isolated groups.

That is certainly so in man. It is impossible to imagine how else the different races of human beings could have originated. Now I am inclined to think that an analogous thing has happened, or is happening, both with the African anthropoids and with the orangutan – that variations which were 'continuous' are apt to become predominant in groups through isolation, and that to this process in nature are to be ascribed the different local 'races' of the big apes.

It is hardly necessary to point out that, if this proved to be true, there is no similar persistent process discernible anywhere in nature in species subject to rigorous natural selection. Among

---

[1] [We must again recall that in Marais's time no other study of wild apes or monkeys had yet been made. – R.A.]

lower animals, where a distinct variety has been established by natural selection, it is generally kept within its distinct limits by those insurmountable barriers of sexual selection and the sterility of hybrid offspring. I am strongly inclined to think that the offspring of no two sub-races of the same anthropoid will be found to be sterile.[1]

As far as the chacma is concerned, however, there are none of the elements of uncertainty which render the formulation of all such hypotheses with reference to the anthropoids merely tentative suggestions. Our knowledge of this species is wider and more definite, and it can therefore be stated without reservation that:

1) there is greater individual divergence from specific type than in any other non-primate mammal in this country; and

2) the only possible cause of this divergence is the same as that which creates a similar tendency in the domestic animals and man – namely, the ebbing force of natural selection.

It must not be thought that this variability due to protection is confined to the primates and domestic animals. It is a universal law of nature (and its methods of operation have been indicated in this chapter) that *variability increases as the struggle for existence becomes less severe.*

---

[1] In the African anthropoid, as I have suggested, it is even now difficult to draw hard-and-fast classifying lines. I had an opportunity of examining a female called Johanna, whose extraordinary intelligence surprised even those well acquainted with the mentality of the big apes. She was described as a gorilla, but she certainly had more chimpanzee than gorilla characteristics. These were, however, so evenly divided that it was impossible on a superficial examination to say on which side the balance lay.

Under natural conditions there is perhaps no better instance of protection from selection than that afforded by oceanic islands. The isolation and consequent want of immigratory competition, the absence of natural enemies, an equable climate and a plentiful food supply constitute for many species a highly protective environment in such islands. And the result is always the same: extreme variability. And if these varieties are localised, they are often in surprisingly small, contiguous and confined groups.

Most naturalists who have examined the living forms in such islands have been struck by these circumstances. In the Sandwich Islands, for instance, there are over three hundred recorded species of the land mollusc *Achatinella*. Every valley has a localised peculiar variety.

So too in the Celebes – Fritz Sarasin has described the astonishing variation of the same genus, united by an unbroken chain of intermediate forms; and the same thing occurs in higher forms in a great many remote islands.

But although this fact has been observed frequently, the natural law of which it is the result has never been clearly recognised and defined as far as I know – the law that *protection from rigorous selection means a smaller death rate among the variants of a species.*

11

Disturbances of the Sexual Sense

WE TERMED an abnormal manifestation of the sexual sense in the chacma any behaviour which had as its ultimate purpose sexual satisfaction, but which deviated widely from the order found throughout nature and was clearly not beneficial – in that it was not directed to the preservation of the species.

This seemed a common-sense definition, and the use of the word 'abnormal' is justified since, employed in this manner, it will always convey a definite meaning.

It is possible to classify these abnormal manifestations into two main groups:

1) Where the end itself is 'unnatural'; that is, sexual behaviour which aims at satisfaction of the sexual sense but which cannot result in reproduction.

2) Sexual activity which may result in reproduction but where the behaviour involved differs widely from what is normal in the mammalian family.

Both types of abnormality are variations from type, and in both the crucial test is the absence of any benefit from the evolutionary point of view.

It will be recognised that these abnormal manifestations are the invariable accompaniment of protection from selection, just as somatic variations are. They occur in different degrees in domestic animals and man, and their common characteristic is always some form of deterioration.

There is a loss either of the definite purpose of sexual activity,

173

or of a clear direction as to its attainment. And in both instances the loss is disadvantageous since reproduction, the reason for all activity of the sexual sense in nature, is always adversely affected.

It does not seem an irrational assumption that this process, if progressive in a species, must end in sterility, since individuals exhibiting extreme forms of these variations are certainly sterile. These sexual abnormalities must therefore be regarded as continuous psychological variations correlated to, and due to the same causes as, the physical variability described in *Chapter 10*.

Although I propose to deal chiefly with more or less extreme variations, the average expression of the sexual sense in the chacma – what would ordinarily be called the 'normal' – will also have to be discussed in order to make clear the degree and nature of each variation. This usual or average sexual behaviour is in itself in many respects quite abnormal – almost as abnormal as it is in man.

In certain fundamental characteristics, sexual behaviour is uniform throughout nature, and it is in just these characteristics that primate behaviour often deviates widely. The nature and extent of these deviations in the chacma will become clear from the following description.

General Sexual Behaviour

The predominant place which the sexual sense assumes in the life of the chacma is remarkable. There is nothing among the gregarious mammals resembling it. 'Lascivious as a baboon' is a popular saying in this country, and although the accuser does not come into court with overly clean hands, the implied charge is certainly not baseless.

The limitation of season, the determining condition of a natural outward stimulus, the exclusion of the extremely old, and the entire absence of the sexual sense prior to the maturing of the sexual organs – all limit the actual activity of the sexual sense in gregarious mammals to a relatively small fraction of their lives. For the chacma, these restraints no longer exist.

The common order in nature is that the operation of the sexual sense, in both male and female, is in the nature of a pure reflex. Among most gregarious mammals, certain physiological changes take place in the female once annually, and serve to excite her sexual sense. These changes in the female are communicated to the male, primarily through the sense of smell, and stimulate his sexual sense by reflex action.

How completely reflex sexual activity is can be proved experimentally in most of the higher gregarious mammals. If the male is kept from contact with the female, the sexual sense remains dormant. There may be certain psychological disturbances which are generally associated with abstention during times when the female is usually in season, but sexual behaviour itself never becomes apparent. Also, if the sense of smell is destroyed, it can take several years before the sexual sense can be stimulated by sight alone, and even then there is a marked lessening in its responsiveness and vigour. If sight and smell are removed, the sexual sense is rendered permanently inoperative.

The chacma can be excited without natural outward stimulus, and even when all sensory contact with the outside world is cut off (except taste and touch) the sexual sense can still become active and find expression in behaviour. It would seem, therefore, that in the soul of the chacma, these pleasurable sensations have become an ordinary causal memory, and the sexual sense reacts to that memory. The chacma is, in other words, capable of being excited from within, and is no longer dependent upon outward stimulation.

This circumstance is responsible for a great deal of what is unusual and unnatural in the sexual behaviour of the species.

It is hardly necessary to state that the baboon is anything but monogamous. Indeed, a leading characteristic of their sexual life is an apparently inherent and insistent desire for change. Mating always commences with a great show of sexual passion, often more noticeable in the female than in the male. At this early stage the male is more genuinely altruistic than in any other relationship, with perhaps one exception: his care and defence of the young members of the troop.[1]

He will guard the female of his choice with the utmost devotion, and will even on occasion allow her to share his food – the high water mark of baboon unselfishness! This devotion lasts for perhaps a week.

In the female it may be of longer duration, but in the conscience of the male, conjugal fidelity has an airy existence. His roving eye soon begins to rest appraisingly upon the unattached females – if such there be – and, like a lordly pasha, he graciously permits them to display their charms competitively before him. What exactly determines his final choice is hard to surmise. Certainly there is no trace of human aestheticism under similar conditions. Youth and its comeliness have no especial attractions for him. As often as not, he will discard a lusty young female for some ancient harridan, grey and scarred, who ought, judged even by a baboon standard, to be considered ugly.

Nor is the female free from the reproach of conjugal infidelity – of an even worse type, because with her the element of furtiveness often becomes conspicuous. It is true that in many

---

[1] High altruism also appears in battles in defence of the troop. Dogs and even leopards are sometimes attacked by the big males with reckless courage.

instances she will endeavour to retain the wandering affections of her mate by all the blandishments common to her sex, and will sometimes fall into paroxysms of jealous rage directed against her newly selected rival.

But this single-hearted devotion to the temporary lord of her choice rarely illustrates her whole 'love life'. She is frequently guilty of the grossest infidelity while the devotion of her master is at flood tide, and we had many opportunities of studying her behaviour under these circumstances. The object of her guilty passion is generally some young male, nervous and extremely discreet, who has been watching the antics of the paired couple from a safe distance. With cleverness worthy of a better cause, the female will take instant advantage of a little laxity in her mate's watchfulness, and entice the young cavalier to some safe and hidden spot, there to indulge her illicit passion. Even the female who never seems to be unfaithful generally accepts with complacency the sequestration of her master's affection and she invariably calms down very quickly after her initial exhibition of jealous temper.

There is a continuous decline in sexual passion – in the male especially – as each mating runs its course. It becomes apparent that he suffers from *ennui*. The everlasting sameness begins to pall. It ends in complete indifference, abstention and even aversion, before the separation *a mensa et toro* is complete. But the scene alters when his overtures have been accepted by a new female. Then his passion is once more characterised by its original vigour.

Nor does the female after such a divorce spend her days in unprofitable repining. She seeks, and generally soon finds, solace for her lacerated affections in the embrace of some other male.

*

177

It will be realised that in such a community male parental affection as it exists among monogamous animals is an unknown quantity; it is inconceivable, for even if true parental affection did exist, it would indeed be a wise baboon father who knew his own child.

But a form of it does exist, and it is under the stress of this that males attain their highest manifestation of pure altruism. What, in the nature of things, they lack in individual parental affection is quite made up for by a common concern for all the young ones of the troop.

It is a potent and real passion. The big males will cuddle and caress the young indiscriminately, and will carry the heavier ones on long marches or flights after the mothers begin to show signs of exhaustion. If an infant is separated from its mother on the sudden appearance of danger, she will, if extremely hard pressed, desert her child – but only if the big males happen to be in her vicinity. She seems to know, and to expect that they will carry it out of danger. And this they do, sometimes fearlessly and even recklessly risking their lives in the attempt to save a young one. If the big males are not present, the mother will desert her baby only as a last resort, and never until she has made some attempt to hide it.

Variations

Duration of intercourse

It will have been gathered from the foregoing that for the male chacma there is practically no cessation of sexual intercourse. It is continuous throughout the year, unlimited by either season or organic conditions.[1]

But in the female sexual intercourse is, generally speaking, limited by pregnancy, although she certainly continues for a considerable period after conception. The actual time, however, varied greatly and it was difficult to arrive at an average under natural conditions. However, one thing was beyond doubt: intercourse continued for a longer period after conception than in any other mammal. In some extreme cases it took place at an advanced period of gestation.[2] We even saw a case of abortion which my colleague was inclined to attribute to this extraordinary practice.

Barrenness in the female

There were only four mature females in our troop who had no babies and who did not give birth to any during the period of our observation. One of these will be described next as an example of gross physical and sexual aberration. One of the remaining three was the only individual in the troop who had an obvious physical disease: a large swelling on the side of the neck and throat. She was afterwards shot and it was found that

---

[1] [This would be true only in as abnormally large a troop as Marais lived with, since in smaller troops fewer females limit opportunity. – R.A.]
[2] It seems hardly necessary to point out that this is, to the naturalist, a startling abnormality. The inflexible rule in nature is that sexual intercourse ceases as soon as conception has taken place. Not that the female purposely avoids the male, but she cannot excite his sexual sense. The domestic animals afford the only exception among the lower animals.

179

the appearance was due to the enlargement of the right lobe of the thyroid gland, accompanied by a calcareous deposit. The degeneration was recognised by an expert as characteristic of goitre in the human subject.[1]

As in the normal males, so in these barren females sexual intercourse suffered no seasonal interruption.

Monstrosity

The fourth barren female was remarkable as regards both sexual and physical variation. She was the largest and heaviest member of the troop. I have certainly never seen as big a baboon anywhere else. She must have been extremely old. The hairs on the head and chest were quite grey, and at a distance appeared white. With the exception of sexual activity, her behaviour was quite masculine. She was originally mistaken for a male and classed as such in our records.

She was especially interesting because in sexual behaviour she was normally feminine, but in our mistaken classification she appeared to be the only instance of complete inversion of the sexual sense lasting into maturity. She associated with the dominant males only, took part in their battles and raids, and in times of danger showed real masculine courage and determination. Even after we discovered her true sex, she was still of interest, as regards both her sexual behaviour and her unending and restless activity. Her great bodily strength gave her a baboon right of interference in any mating which attracted her attention, and these were of daily occurrence. With determined threats of violence she would capture and carry off the unfortunate male and by the same means enforce his fidelity for perhaps half a day.

---

[1] There were at the time several cases of human goitre in the vicinity.

When her true sex was discovered she was nicknamed 'The Prostitute' by a native servant, and retained this title of distinction to the end.

After her behaviour had been carefully noted, she was separated from the troop and shot. It was then found that the shape of the body and musculature were normally masculine. The masculine occipital and orbital ridges were excessively developed and the condition of the masculine canine teeth testified to her great age. The mammae were quite undeveloped and masculine in shape. On dissection, no trace of hermaphroditism was disclosed. The ovaries and sexual organs generally were normally feminine.

Sexual periodicity

Sexual periodicity in the female chacma is generally of irregular occurrence, and frequency seems to be to a great extent determined by environmental conditions. During droughts and times of food scarcity the irregularity seemed to increase and the frequency to lessen. The opposite occurs during times of plenty and ease. The time of greatest sexual excitement in both male and female coincides with the sexual period in the female. In this the behaviour of the chacma is similar to that of all the non-primate mammals, but there the analogy ends.

Outside the order of primates, sexual activity is strictly limited by the duration of this period in the female. Even when conception does not take place, the organic changes which constitute the condition run a certain definite course and then cease, whereupon all intercourse stops. In other words, sexual activity in the male is only reactive to the sexual condition in the female, and in the absence of that definite stimulus it remains dormant.

In many gregarious mammals, males under natural conditions

exhibit certain secondary types of sexual behaviour during the time the female would be in season, apparently even in her absence. Calling, restlessness and fighting with other males often reveals profound psychic disturbances. But one rule remains absolute in nature: there can be no excitation of primary sexual activity in the male without the presence of the female when her organic changes are in progress.

The behaviour of the chacma affords startling exceptions to this rule. Although the sexual period in the female initiates the greatest activity of the sexual sense in both male and female, intercourse is not limited by that occurrence. It can and does frequently take place outside the period; and although conception automatically puts an end to the condition in the female, conception itself, as I have said, is no immediate and final bar to further sexual intercourse, as is the case with all other mammals.

In most of the lower African primates the sexual period is characterised by turgescence in the female and a great increase in the brilliant sexual coloration which is generally common in both sexes. In the chacma this coloration is very inconspicuous when compared with that of lower forms. In the male it is absent and in the female it occurs only during the sexual period. In the African anthropoids it has been permanently lost in both sexes.

It is quite evident that in the lower mammals the sexual period serves one, and apparently *only* one, beneficial purpose. The accompanying discharge is highly odoriferous and powerfully excites the sexual impulse in the male through his sense of smell. Where the sexes are normally segregated during the sexual period the males are able to follow and find the females, though often separated by vast distances, guided solely by the compelling odour.

So it seems clear that the vivid sexual coloration in the

primates, which invariably attains extreme brilliance in the female during the sexual period, is intimately connected with the degeneration of the sense of smell. None of the higher South African primates can trace the female by the sense of smell alone.

A male chacma was not excited by a female during the sexual period when she was hidden a few feet from him behind a screen of matting. However, the moment he was allowed to see her sexual coloration, he became strongly excited. It would seem, therefore, that as the sense of smell decayed, an appeal to the sense of sight was selected in its place. And in the chacma, the anthropoids and man (in whom the sexual sense can be excited without the need of any outward stimulation) even this sexual coloration appeal to sight has either been lost – as in the two latter species – or has become of comparatively little importance, as in the chacma.

It seems certain that somewhere in man's phyletic history this appeal, first to smell by means of sexual odours, and thereafter to sight by means of sexual coloration, must have existed. It would be difficult to account for the persistence of half-oriented survivals in the human being on any other assumption.

Deep in his psychic history lies the cause which determines his 'aesthetic' taste in colour and perfume. And this taste is beyond any shadow of a doubt sexual in origin. Not by mere chance does the lady of Babylon select her glowing raiment or make her person fragrant with castor, musk and civet – the sexual perfumes common to all the lower mammals. Dr Havelock Ellis (in *Man and Woman*) points out that in many women, the whole skin becomes fragrant during the sexual period. This is clearly an organic survival which accompanies the psychological one I have described.

The gradual modification of the female sexual period in the

primates can be studied in practically all its stages in existing species. In many lower forms the discharge is odoriferous and still serves to excite the male through his sense of smell. As one ascends to higher forms, the odour is lost and colour, often excessive and flamboyant, takes its place. There is always an accompanying and proportionate degeneration of the sense of smell. In the male the sense no longer serves any great sexual purpose, and in these higher forms it is also difficult to see any anatomical or environmental use in the female discharge. These modifications have reached an extreme point in the African anthropoids and man.

Birth

The female chacma about to give birth often separated herself from the troop and selected some secluded spot for the purpose. We noticed on several occasions that where she was accompanied by an independent older offspring, she would persistently and often cruelly drive it away from her a few days previously. This always served as a sure indication that the birth was about to take place.

The degree of pain accompanying birth varied greatly. In some individuals – even in a first pregnancy – the infant made its appearance with ease and celerity, and a minimum of trouble and pain, comparable only to the more happy condition of the lower mammals.

In other cases there was deep maternal suffering quite human-like in its intensity and its methods of expression. It seems, however, quite beyond doubt that birth pain is more severe in the chacma than in any other mammal outside the order of the primates. Some degree of pain apparently always exists in vertebrate reproduction; but there certainly seems to be a gradual increase in intensity for the higher mammals through the lower primates to man.

It is hardly possible to consider these facts without coming to the puzzling question of origin. Why should pain have been selected at all in connection with this supreme function of organic existence? What benefit was there to the individual or the race?

There can be little doubt that in lower forms of organic beings, the process of reproduction is as simple as it is painless. Where, for instance, the expulsion of the ova takes place as simply and with as little accentuation in behaviour as any ordinary vital process, the presence of any sensation approximating pain is hardly conceivable.

And it is in these cases where reproduction is unaccompanied by any manifestation of pain – where even the fertilisation of the ova is left to chance – that there is also an entire absence of the maternal instinct.

The fate of the embryo is left to the tender mercies of its natural environment and the device of producing vast numbers has generally been selected, in place of the later-evolved maternal care, to ensure the continuation of the species. It is only in higher forms, with a greatly reduced birth rate, that the first indications of birth pain are met, and as a sure and proportionate accompaniment there is always the care of the immature young by the mother. It seems safe to say that among species under natural conditions, the greater the birth pain, the higher becomes the maternal instinct.

Now, it is a rule in nature which will be familiar to every student of comparative psychology that every hereditary instinct needs an outward suggestion or stimulus to bring it into operation. The stronger this suggestion is, the more potent is the reaction of the instinct. This is especially so with instincts which become active in the mammals only at a late stage of development, such as those connected with the procuring of food and the sexual sense. These cannot originally become operative except in response to a stimulus from without.[1]

This seems to me the selective purpose of birth pain among higher organic forms. It serves to call into instant activity the maternal instinct. It seems reasonable to assume that in order to ensure the safety of the offspring – a thing of supreme importance to the race – an appeal should be selected to the most compelling sensation of which higher organisms are capable, and that this compelling sensation should serve the purpose of fixing the mother's attention on her helpless offspring and calling into being the complex of emotions constituting the maternal instinct.

The connection of birth pain and maternal love is apparent as a dimly conscious idea in the human soul. In the first 'yearning' over her newborn babe, I suggest, there is often strongly present in the mind of the human mother a conviction that the love and tenderness she feels has some sure but dimly understood relation to the agony she has endured. The literature of all peoples and all times bears witness to this association of ideas.

At different times we observed and recorded several facts about mammalian reproduction which tended to corroborate this interpretation of the phenomenon of birth pain. For instance, one season we kept under observation a herd of cattle and a flock of sheep in which the 'casting away' of calves and lambs was prevalent. The majority of the mothers who obstinately refused

---

[1] [Contemporary ethology of the Lorenz-Tinbergen school speaks of the releaser and the innate releasing mechanism. – R.A.]

to receive or recognise their offspring were among those which we had classified as having had an 'easy and painless birth'. Those with a strong and correctly directed maternal instinct were invariably individuals which had shown suffering during parturition. It seemed as if in these cases the strength of the evoked instinct was in proportion to the degree of pain suffered.

Immature intercourse

The chacma often showed primary sexual activity sometime before reaching maturity and we recorded actual intercourse between immature males and females on several occasions. Even more startling was what amounted to forced intercourse between mature males and immature females. During our observations several such instances were observed, and they resulted in severe injuries to the immature female because of her desperate resistance and the violence of the mature male.

These seemed to be in the nature of impulsive acts and were not characterised by the usual mating behaviour of the males. There was no evidence that this process was ever repeated by the same two individuals, perhaps chiefly due to the terror inspired in the young female by the first attempt. She took good care that there was no opportunity for a repetition.

Other instances were observed where the dominant males intervened in the defence of a threatened immature female, and it is possible that these unnatural assaults would have occurred more frequently had it not been for this deterrent.

Homosexuality

Actual homosexual intercourse occurred among the young males that had just reached sexual maturity. It seemed that their inability to secure mature females until fighting powers were fully developed (and that was always long after sexual maturity) may probably have been one of the causes of this behaviour.

But it must be borne in mind that the disadvantage which young males suffer in the sexual struggle is common to all the higher mammals, and yet outside the order of primates one looks in vain for actual homosexual intercourse under natural conditions. It is more likely that the real cause is psychological and is because the sexual sense in the chacma can be excited without natural outward stimulus.

In homosexual encounters among the chacma, the younger and weaker male always voluntarily assumed the female role and the older and more mature, the male.

Similar homosexual tendencies were observed in immature females. Here it was always the outcome of long-established affectionate friendship. The physical completion of the act was, of course, impossible and it seemed more like an impulsive action in which there was no real sexual excitement involved. In this respect it differed very widely from male homosexual intercourse.

This behaviour is, I think, very closely allied to a tendency often observed in captive baboons: attempted intercourse with non-primate mammals – that is, with domestic animals irrespective of sex. Both male and female chacmas reveal this tendency on occasion, accompanied by strong excitement.

A study of chacma behaviour makes it seem more than likely that the attitude of sexual exhibition, which is common throughout the mammals and absolutely hereditary, has some connection with both male homosexual tendencies and intercourse with non-primate animals.

The attitude of sexual exhibition is common and identical in both sexes of the chacma. Artificially reared babies adopt it from their earliest years. It is the common attitude not of sexuality but of conciliation both in captivity and under natural conditions, and is generally adopted in captivity for the purpose of begging or imploring.

When a larger and stronger individual, male or female, pursues in anger a smaller and weaker baboon of either sex, the latter when cornered or exhausted will invariably assume the attitude of sexual exhibition. Its effect is often instantaneous and very remarkable. The anger of the pursuer usually subsides at once, and in most cases where the rage of the pursuer is not excessive, the threatened individual will escape chastisement by the adoption of this method of imploring pity.

But its psychological effect is evidently varied. In most cases the pursuer becomes calm, and there is no behaviour to show that he takes any further notice of the object of his anger. In some cases, however, the attitude has the effect of immediately arousing the sexual sense of the pursuer and consequent behaviour clearly shows that sexual feeling is instantly substituted for rage.

It is true that we never saw consummated homosexual intercourse under these conditions, but tentative efforts were common. It seems unlikely, therefore, that the homosexual habit (if we can speak of it as such) is acquired as a result of this behaviour. But all these circumstances certainly do seem to cooperate in the creation of homosexual habits. They are in the nature of favourable environmental circumstances reacting on a predisposed psychological condition.

One more observation remains to be mentioned which, from an analogous result in the case of man, would lead one to infer that it also had a great influence in establishing homosexual tendencies in the male chacmas of our troop. It must be made clear that the troop was completely isolated and had apparently been so for many years, and during the period of our observation the mature males always exceeded the mature females in numbers. In man, the absence of females is undoubtedly a determining factor in the establishment of homosexual tendencies. Professor Edvard Westermarck (*Origin and Development of Moral Ideas*), who of all modern writers has compiled the most systematic, perhaps the most complete history of homosexuality from the anthropological point of view in man, repeatedly traces homosexual practices to this cause.[1]

Another interesting observation we made was in connection with acquired homosexuality and inversion of the sexual sense. No chacma, either in captivity or under natural conditions, exhibited a congenital and unchangeable inversion, nor was there any case where long-continued homosexual practices brought about an inversion. In all cases, as soon as heterosexual intercourse commenced, all homosexual tendencies ceased.

Whatever the condition of man may be, it seems to me very unlikely that there is such a thing as congenital inversion of the

---

[1] [Contemporary primate students discount actual homosexuality in the wild baboon. The postures Marais observed, common not only in primate but in rodent species, seem to be performed in a social rather than sexual context. He was correct in his interpretation of conciliation, and he may well have been correct that the abnormal structure of his troop encouraged abnormal practices. But all observation today would indicate, for example, that the mounting by one male of another tends to be an affirmation of social dominance on the part of the one, and social submission on the part of the other. – R.A.]

sexual sense in the chacma at all, or that acquired homosexuality in this primate exercises any permanent modifying effect on the sexual sense. We certainly obtained no evidence justifying such a conclusion.

Deorientation

While investigating the extent to which phyletic memories persist in the chacma, we came across the wholly unexpected fact that there are cases in which there is absolutely no hereditary orientation of the sexual sense. These experiments had necessarily to be made with artificially reared baboons.

We found that in about half our subjects, the most vital instincts were not transmitted, as they are in the lower African primates and in all non-primate mammals. These subjects did not know their natural food, nor when or how to look for it. They could not recognise any environmental danger, could not distinguish beasts of prey, and they showed no fear of snakes – the one thing that was certainly and strongly hereditary in many individuals. They were, in fact, quite helpless when released in their natural environment.

What is known of the psychology of the anthropoids led us to anticipate some such condition in the chacma. But nothing had led us to anticipate that primary sexual behaviour would be other than hereditary.

The individuals lacking this most essential of all phyletic memories after attaining maturity had to gain their sexual knowledge with great difficulty under direct and continued suggestion. They had, in fact, to learn all that was necessary for sexual intercourse, just as they had to learn a new relation of cause and effect.

Invariably the sexual sense was powerfully excited by a female, but there was absolutely no hereditary knowledge of the natural method of satisfaction. There is every reason to believe that this loss of the inborn direction of the sexual sense has proceeded much further than in the chacma. Whereas in the latter species the individuals who show a complete absence of all instinctive knowledge are rare, in man probably the great majority are subject to this singular psychological degeneration. And when we come to secondary sexual behaviour, then it is quite certain that no single human being comes into existence with any trace of inborn knowledge.[1]

In the lower primates and the mammals in general, each individual is born completely equipped with both primary and secondary sexual direction. They know without the need of any experience or teaching the natural method of satisfying the sexual sense, they know the right season, the period of abstention and all the organic conditions of the female that begin and end sexual intercourse, and the behaviour is always identical in all individuals.

Man has to be taught all this, and the teaching varies as widely as the races of mankind do. Most savage races have initiation ceremonies during which primary and secondary sexual behaviour is taught to both sexes as they reach maturity, and I do not think

---

[1] [Marais seems to have been the first to discover the sexual helplessness of primates raised in isolation from their kind. Similar observations by others furnished psychology with its argument that man has no instincts, and that even sex is learned behaviour. Only in recent years has it been demonstrated that the problem is not one of learning, but of neurosis. Male rhesus monkeys raised in isolation by Harry F. Harlow at the University of Wisconsin have been incapable not only of sexual orientation but of intromission. Yet rhesus orphans, raised without adult contact but with opportunity to play together, display no sexual inadequacy. To my best knowledge, there has not yet been an experiment with baboons. – R.A.]

that there are any two tribes in which the teaching is identical. And what the savage teaches in sexual behaviour would certainly not find favour in our existing civilisations.

It is quite common, for instance, among great numbers of savage peoples to teach and provide means for homosexual relations just as if they were the natural expression of the sexual sense in man. The teaching varies just as widely on such questions as monogamy, the continuance of intercourse after conception has taken place, cessation during menstruation, etc.

Two things are apparent in both the savage and the civilised sexual teachings of man, and both are of supreme interest to the comparative psychologist.

First, there is a laborious striving after more natural behaviour. In other words, man, bearing no knowledge within himself, strives and strives to imitate the sexual behaviour of the lower animals. In all so-called scientific teaching as well, such behaviour has been set as a standard. It is, of course, the only standard available.

The second interesting fact is the idea of something wrong, something evil in the sexual sense itself. It is certainly apparent in all great religious systems. In Buddhism abstention is a virtue, and indulgence is a source of spiritual pollution. In the Muslim and Jewish religions sexual intercourse causes ceremonial impurity. The Hebrew myth of Adam and Eve has as a central idea the inherent evil of sexual intercourse. It is a forbidden thing, not only a sin in itself, but imparting its contaminating influence to the individual resulting from it.

The idea reaches its supreme point in the Christian religion, where it is regarded as an undesirable evil. The Apostle Paul teaches that it is a hindrance to man's spiritual regeneration, and in the Fourteenth Chapter of the Revelation of St John, the description of a multitude of souls redeemed from the earth reads: "These are they which were not defiled with women; for they are virgins".

Hence, too, the doctrine of the immaculate conception and the continuous virginity of Mary. Christ, born of no natural sexual intercourse, was the one being who appeared on the earth uncontaminated by this thing that had fallen upon man as the primal and supreme curse.

But these ideas underlying man's sexual teaching, the idea of a natural standard and the idea of inherent evil in sexuality itself, are of interest to the comparative psychologist for the reason that both conceptions reveal the extent to which deorientation has progressed and the teaching become an ambiguous instruction. Phyletic memory being incomplete, man must look to causal memory for an answer. And man is left without firm moral direction derived from natural order.

Masturbation

Masturbation in some troops occurred among the younger mature members of both sexes. Outside the temporarily paired adults, the average was somewhere in the neighbourhood of ten per cent of the sexually mature. Masturbation was more certainly idiocratic than homosexuality – that is, it was more certainly a habit of the individual and not, as in the case of homosexuality, apparently a tendency to which all were at times subject.

It was often observed in our wild troop under certain definite circumstances. A young male would fall in love with a much older mated female, and would follow her persistently at a considerable distance. Any sexual advances by the older male who at the time happened to be the master of her affections would throw the watchful cavalier into a state of intense excitement, which, however, never exceeded the bounds of extreme discretion.

Under such conditions masturbation was frequently resorted to. It sometimes happened that the female in question would make secret advances to her distant admirer, but if masturbation had become a habit he would very rarely take advantage of this natural means of satisfaction. The approach of the female would induce a state of nervous apprehension and he would generally assume the female sexual attitude, which was apparently protective. But if the young male had not resorted to the practice of masturbation, he would invariably take immediate advantage of the proffered natural means of satisfaction.

It must not be inferred, however, that these circumstances always accompanied or preceded the practice of masturbation in an individual. The most that my experience justifies me in saying is that we observed the connection between this definite set of circumstances and the practice in a great many instances. My colleague was inclined to the view that where the practice was indulged in for any length of time before the male succeeded in attaining sexual satisfaction naturally, it had certain well-marked neurotic results. Such an individual became solitary in his ways, morose, and vicious in temper. Physically, too, there was almost immediately a falling off in condition even when food was plentiful.

I was not quite satisfied myself that this did occur under natural conditions. In captivity there is no doubt that the habit invariably produces a morose and vicious temper.

About two per cent of those addicted to the practice of masturbation at any one time were females.

Among older mature adults who had already mated it was

never observed, but in captive baboons kept under conditions where the natural means of sexual satisfaction were wanting, masturbation was far more common and had no age limit, and very often the habit could be directly traced to initiation by example. On the other hand, we could not find any absolute proof that the habit ever occurred spontaneously in any individual. It is quite possible that it may have been conveyed to certain troops by baboons who had acquired the habit in captivity. Among wild troops living remote from human habitation, it was not observed.

Sexual impulses in captivity

A noticeable fact among baboons kept in captivity was the predominance of the sexual sense in older females kept from contact with males. This rose to fever pitch during the sexual periods. At such times a female will eagerly and persistently offer herself to every male human being who approaches her. She distinguishes between male and female, and towards women she often shows a vicious hostility. Masturbation in such cases – when it does occur, and it is very rare – seems to be generally a reaction to strong physical irritation.

In man, the metamorphosis of emotion is even rarer than in the chacma. The best-known examples are the sexual perversions known as masochism and sadism, respectively. In masochism pain and humiliation are changed into sexual excitement, and in extreme types of sadism there occurs a transformation of sexual excitement into rage and bloodlust.

It must not be thought that by using the word 'transformation' any theoretical psychological explanation is implied. I must acknowledge that the tendency is a mystery to me. From an evolutionary point of view I am unable to explain it, and we found no facts from which its phyletic history could be inferred.

The earlier observers into human sexual abnormalities explained sadism on the theoretical assumption that the sex and anger centres are nearly related and that in these cases either the stimulus is sent to the wrong centre, or the excitation of one centre affects the other, or the stimulus excites the nearly related afferent nerves much in the same way as an induced current does.

The evolutionist would describe sadism as a phyletic survival of which the origin is seen in the sex-battles of the lower animals, and that is perhaps the same thing in other words. But even this explanation, such as it is, becomes doubtful when one realises that in lower primates the tendency is much more pronounced, and that emotions are involved which are not in any way related.

THE END

MY FRIENDS THE BABOONS

1
The Habits of Baboons

IN NO SPECIES of animal is greater interest being taken at present by scientific investigators than in the apes. The inquiry is being directed especially towards acquiring information about the habits of apes in their natural environment, and it is precisely herein that opportunities, and consequently our knowledge, are lacking. We know less about the habits of apes than about those of almost any other land animal.

The reason for this is of course the inaccessibility of most apes. In all countries, except Africa, the apes are inhabitants of the densest woods and jungles where it is impossible to keep them in sight for more than a few minutes at a time. Unless one is able to watch animals for days on end uninterrupted, it is not possible to discover the secrets of their behaviour.

A great deal is done by means of experiments in captivity, but it is under just such conditions that the ape is the most difficult of all animals to study.

Its psychological development enables it – as it does man – to adjust itself rapidly to any new environment. In captivity it soon learns all kinds of new habits and its general behaviour alters so completely that it is impossible to deduce from its behaviour in captivity what its habits would be in its natural state.

There is only one species of ape in the world that can easily be studied in its natural surroundings – if the investigator makes use of the favourable conditions – and that is our South African baboon. Our baboon was, of course, an arboreal animal originally, and it is still frequently encountered as a true arboreal animal in our large woods and along river banks. But the greater part of the race has long since taken flight to the 'everlasting hills', whence it can in safety defy all its enemies, man included. For more than a hundred years, with all the resources with which science has equipped him, man has waged a relentless war against the baboon, and still it survives, even in those regions where the war has raged most fiercely.

And not only does the baboon continue to exist, but it has acquired in the short period of a single lifetime new habits, which make it, in many places, the most dangerous enemy against which the farmer has to contend in his struggle for existence.

Where at first it confined its hostile activities to orchards and grain lands (for the baboon is by nature a plant and insect-eater) it has since acquired the knowledge, under the pressure of drought and famine, that food is to be found in the animals kept by man.

Its natural aversion to flesh has prevented it thus far from becoming, in certain parts, wholly a beast of prey – but not everywhere, as will be seen later. It discovered that nourishing milk was to be found in the stomachs of lambs.

It is about eighty years ago that the baboon made its first appearance in South Africa in the role of a catcher of lambs, and then only in the drier areas of the central Cape Province. In no other portion of South Africa did it acquire this habit of its own accord. It is, for instance, unknown to this day in the northern Transvaal, but from the Karroo this evil spread slowly northwards until nowadays it is a regular habit right up to the Vaal River.

But almost daily, new habits are acquired. In the Suikerbosrand, for instance, where a troop of baboons has had to wage a terrible struggle for existence against the steady encroachment over its territory by man, the baboons have had recourse, within the last ten years, to other means of subsistence.

Hitherto they had caught lambs only to tear open the entrails and eat the curdled milk.

But in Heidelberg, during past years this had not proved a sufficient source of food for the beleaguered troop. They then began to eat the flesh of the slaughtered lambs, and to-day lambs are captured in the Suikerbosrand for no other purpose.

The method of slaughter has changed astonishingly. The lamb is no longer killed by tearing open the entrails: it is stretched out on its back, both jugular veins are carefully exposed and severed by biting, and then the animal is left until it is dead and the veins are emptied of blood, for it seems that the baboon still has a dislike of blood. Thereafter the lamb is properly skinned (in a manner in which no beast of prey could do it) and the flesh torn from the limbs and eaten.

The meat-eating habits in the Suikerbosrand appear to be spreading daily in other directions. A short while ago the baboons there discovered that the full-grown sheep makes as satisfactory a victim as the helpless lamb, so they now slaughter large sheep; and not only sheep, but pigs, ducks, fowls, guinea-fowls, and turkeys are already on the list of their booty in the Suikerbosrand.

The reader will realise at once that there is no other species of animal in its natural state which exhibits such changes of habit. In Australia there is a parrot which plucked the wool from sheep to line its nest. By chance it acquired a taste for flesh, and now it attacks sheep for their meat. This is sometimes cited as the greatest change of habit in nature, but it cannot compare with what appears in baboons.

It is just these changes of habit which make it so essential (and at the same time so difficult), to study the ape in its natural environment.

What makes the study of the apes of such urgent importance lies hidden in a very self-seeking reason – as is usual with man.

In the scientific world, the belief is steadily gaining ground that the continuance of man's existence on earth is in immediate danger. All new knowledge seems to provide further proof that the threatened destruction of man lies within calculable time. I shall endeavour to explain shortly the general opinion of 'organised science' on this matter.

It is contended, sometimes, that purpose and reason are apparent in the evolution of man; that he is the perfect product, the goal towards which organic evolution has been striving through all these millions of years. This notion arises from the erroneous idea that evolution always strives towards a condition of absolute perfection. All that evolution can bring about in an organism is to fit it, by selection, for one or other definite natural environment.

Among contemporary mammals there is perceptible a 'psychological' evolution in the direction of freeing, psychologically, the species from the disadvantage of restriction to a limited environment in which a sudden change (of climate, for example) may lead to extinction. This psychological development tends to destroy all inherited environmental knowledge (instinct) and to make the organism dependent on individually acquired environmental knowledge.

The immediate benefit to any species in which this form of evolution is taking place is to enable such a species to take refuge in any natural environment differing from that in which it would otherwise be easily able to live, there immediately to learn the new knowledge which is essential for its existence.

Apes, anthropoid apes, and man have progressed furthest in the direction of this psychological development. That is why man can live both in the Sahara desert and on the polar ice; that is why we find the baboons on the fruitful mountains of the Cape Peninsula, the snow-covered ridges of the Drakensberg, in the large forests as a true arboreal animal, and in the middle of the drought-stricken areas of the Kalahari desert.

Like all other animals on earth, man must pay dearly for this psychological development towards freedom from a limited natural environment. His reason gives him the power to protect himself by virtue of acquired environmental knowledge and the destruction of inherited environmental knowledge (instincts) against all natural conditions hostile to him.

But it is only by the operation of hostile nature that selection within a species can take place, and it is only by selection that the type of the race can be preserved. In many instances it has been proved experimentally that those individuals of a race which vary furthest from type are the first to perish when a sudden change in environment takes place. In America it has been shown by measurements that of the thousands of birds that die during sudden storms almost every one varies distinctly from type in one or other direction.

On the other hand, all animals which enjoy a high degree of protection show a correspondingly high degree of individual variation from type.

On some islands of the Pacific, there are indigenous insects which have no natural enemies, and the climate is so equable and favourable that deaths among the insects are never due to sudden environmental changes. The result is that in all the mountain valleys, separated often only by a cliff from each other, different kinds of the same species can be found. This can be ascribed only to the fact that here the individuals that vary are never destroyed by unfavourable environmental conditions.

Of any living species of animal, man enjoys the greatest protection against natural selection. Generally speaking, the divergent individual in man enjoys the same measure of protection as the typical one. The result is that among living animal species, man shows the greatest individual variation from type. Put a Chinese, a Negro, a Bushman, and a European together, and no naturalist (without knowing the facts) would ever classify them otherwise than as different animal species, whose crossing would be sterile.

We know, however, that they are merely group variations of precisely the same kind and species.

Individual variations, too, are as wide as group variations. In all human races there are giants and dwarfs, geniuses and idiots. There are greater variations in bodily measurements than in any other animal species. Even in the internal organs of different individuals, enormous variations are found.

After man, we should naturally expect to find the greatest variation from type in the anthropoid apes and the other apes, because they enjoy exactly the same kind of protection, by reason of the same remarkable type of psychological development.

And this is so. Our increasing knowledge of the anthropoid apes has long since established this fact. On two mountain ranges which lie within sight of each other in Central Africa, two races of gorilla are found so different from each other that one would almost be inclined to classify them as separate species. The difference, however, is merely the result of variations from type. Among the few anthropoid apes which man has kept in captivity during the past fifty years, individual variations' have in many cases been found greater than in any other known species of animal except man.

There is no doubt that variations from type of this kind are the first and at the same time the greatest indication of natural degeneration. In man, this protection and variation has produced more bodily and mental diseases than can be found in any other animal. The fact that protection results in an enormous increase in population does not affect the point. The increase in population is merely a temporary and passing phenomenon, while divergence from type is permanent and irreparable.

It is in this way that nature destroys all races that no longer fit into a natural environment.

The optimistic belief that man is evolving psychologically towards some perfect state is based on an unscientific conception. Without natural selection, there can be no evolution; only degeneration.

Humanity is most certainly on the march towards the madhouse.

Without doubt the increase of mental diseases is greater than that of any other evil that afflicts man. All civilised countries will have to find asylums and money for the maintenance of their steadily growing army of lunatics.

The disappearance of extinct species, which can be ascribed to divergence from type, shows that nature is following an unchanging road. Increase may keep pace with variations, but in nature there is a limit which cannot be overstepped. Suddenly the birth rate falls while the death rate remains unchanged. One would be inclined to expect that as soon as equilibrium had been reached, the birth rate would increase again. But this never happens. As soon as natural extinction sets in, no restoration is possible. It goes on until the whole race, no matter how powerful and well equipped against hostile nature, is forever wiped from the face of the earth.

Thus disappeared the untold number of mammoths that for millions of years possessed the whole earth, so that today science can read the history of their existence and decline only in imperishable rocks. The dinosaurs, protected like armoured cruisers, capable of enjoying an elephant for a meal, whose evolution must have taken countless millions of years and that, once 'perfected', reigned on the earth for further millions of years, have vanished. Of their mighty dominance they have left nothing on earth except a few huge footprints in rocks and some petrified skeletons in old river deposits for the housing of which our largest museums are too small.

There exists not the least doubt in organised science today that the greatest threat to the continuance of man's existence on earth is divergence from type, coupled with increase in population. The protection of divergent individuals increases the natural tendency to vary from type, while the increase in population always results in an increase in the percentage of diverging individuals.

It would be a miracle for modern science if the culminating point of man's existence should prove to be an exception to the unalterable natural law.

If mankind wishes to escape the doom which now threatens its existence on earth – if, in the last ditch, man still wishes to fight unrelenting nature, it will be possible only through the adoption of one strategic measure: the variation from type and the great increase in population must be stopped in some scientific way.

For this purpose, science must be called in, and the first step towards acquiring the necessary knowledge to arm man for his last struggle for existence is a thorough study of the animal species most nearly related to man – the apes and anthropoid apes.

The general reader has often little knowledge of the practical advantages which man has obtained – and still obtains daily – from the study of apes. During the past few years, both in medicine and psychology, our progress has in great measure been due to the use of apes for experimental purposes. The ape is so nearly related to us that he is, actually, the only animal that in all respects exhibits the same physical reactions as man.

In all probability there would not today be any surgeon who had the necessary knowledge and courage to cut out a man's appendix if experimental operations on anthropoid apes had not first of all made it possible and safe. And this is so in hundreds of other of the largest and most important operations which science has made possible at present. The fight against many deadly illnesses has been made possible only by experiments on apes.

The reader will thus realise that the study of the ape in his natural surroundings is not due to mere scientific curiosity. A far greater evil than any disease threatens mankind as a race, and if he hopes to escape it, the study of this evil in its first appearance in the apes is undoubtedly the most promising way.

But to return to the difficulties that make the study so hard and in many instances impossible.

In various parts of the world, attempts are being made at present to obviate the unfavourable influences of captivity by artificially creating a 'natural' environment.

The first attempt was made under the patronage of the Smithsonian Institute at Montecito in California. My advice and help was solicited in this connection, although I prophesied that the experiment would in all probability be a failure for precisely the same reasons that make observations in captivity useless.

A number of South African baboons and other apes were released in a large oak wood under conditions which permitted continual observation of them. My prediction unfortunately came true, and the experiment as a whole could hardly be called a success. The baboons and apes immediately learnt of their own accord all sorts of new habits, and fitted themselves so well to their new environment that their mode of life in it could not be recognised as the same as that of their natural state. Even that usually most unchangeable characteristic in animal life, the growth of the sexual sense, was so changed in the apes in America that this most important natural phenomenon never appeared in them.

In Madeira, a German experimental station for chimpanzees was erected and there was mention of a second in Florida in the United States, but in these stations little effort was made to create a natural environment. The main objective was simply to keep the rare anthropoid apes alive, and to ensure their propagation. The experiments there were limited to such as would give a comparison of their behaviour, psychologically, with that of man.

In the meantime, in South Africa, I took advantage of an opportunity which occurs in no other country – to study baboons intimately and from close at hand.

A few years after the Anglo-Boer War, Mr Alec Austin – a Transvaaler who grew up on the *veld* – and I built a permanent residence in the high-lying valley between the double row of mountains of the well-known farm Doornhoek in Waterberg, where later tin was discovered and mined for years.

The region was a delightful one for the purpose we had in mind, and I do not think that I ever passed a happier time in my life than the three years we spent in the mountains of Doornhoek. The whole of the district of Waterberg was very thinly populated at that time. Moreover, many of the inhabitants were prisoners of war abroad, for repatriation was still in progress, and we were in Waterberg for more than a year before the last of our neighbours appeared again on his farm.

Our dwelling was thus at first very lonely, but the natural beauty of the place more than compensated for this. We were practically separated from the civilised world. There was only one road to our dwelling in the mountain valley, and this was through a *kloof* which at that time was so wild and overgrown that it required great exertion by even a physically fit person to reach the top.

One side the *kloof* was bordered by a *krans*, two or three hundred feet high, and on the other side was a *kop* so steep that it could almost be called a *krans* too. The *kloof* itself was filled with a piled-up mass of huge boulders which in times past had split from the *krans* and tumbled down into the *kloof.* Even while we were there, falls of rock occurred twice, and the noise re-echoed through the mountains like thundering explosions.

The *krans*, the fallen boulders, and every available inch of ground was thickly overgrown with mighty trees and the most beautiful mountain plants that Waterberg could produce. In no other place have I ever seen a more beautiful collection of tree-ferns, and the glory of the flowers at certain seasons was always an astonishing surprise for visitors from the towns.

Flat against the face of the *krans* grew several massive wild fig trees. The roots of these giants lay curled like huge pythons for several hundred feet over the surface of the *krans*. Where the roots obtained the necessary moisture and nourishment for their trees has always remained a mystery to me.

A crystal clear mountain stream came down the valley and found an exit to the flats through the entrance to this *kloof*. The heaped-up boulders turned this stream in the *kloof* into a series of stone- basin waterfalls and cascades.

A troop of about three hundred baboons lived in these mountains of Doornhoek. They had only one fixed sleeping place – a hollow in the *krans*, protected in part by the branches of a large wild fig tree. Here every day at sundown they gathered, unless they were prevented from doing so by leopards, which happened now and again. When this did happen, they spent a sleepless night on the crest of the neighbouring *kop*, and usually we were compelled to keep watch with them.

Mr Austin and I built our huts in the mountain valley a few hundred feet from the upper entrance of the *kloof*, and within a few months we were on such friendly terms with the baboons that we could walk through the troop as a farmer does among his sheep.

They were already fearless when we arrived there because for almost four years – during the Anglo-Boer War – they had not been shot at. Later on, we had to protect them by payment of small amounts to farmers as compensation for pilfered mealies and fruit.

Finally – after a brotherhood of three years – all protection became impossible, and we had to say farewell forever to our friends of the high mountains.

By spreading dry mealies in the grass, we soon made them accustomed to us. The relationship became so intimate that we gained their complete confidence. We knew every full-grown animal, and gave it a name and number on a list. At first we often followed them on their daily journeys through the mountains and by broadcasting mealies now and then, we so delayed their progress that we could keep pace with them.

We also kept a number of tame adults and babies, some in captivity and some at liberty at a farmhouse below the mountains. Later we also had at different times in captivity wild adults that had been wounded by scalp-hunters and captured alive. Under these conditions, their behaviour was studied for a period just exceeding three years.

Ideal as these conditions were in one respect, we yet laboured under disadvantages that were not without effect on our work. The greatest of these was – as it appeared later, the want of time. As the neighbouring farmers regained possession of rifles and ammunition, observation of the troop became more and more difficult and all too soon was rendered quite impossible. Other serious disadvantages were the isolation, the absence of libraries, and the means of ascertaining the nature of work already accomplished in this direction by other researchers.

In this connection, I may be permitted a word as to our own mental attitude in the exploration of these twilight souls. We approached this investigation without any preconceived ideas, and although inexperience at the beginning may have left much to be desired in our methods, we had at least no theories to verify.

We tried under all circumstances to adhere to the empirical method, and to avoid as far as possible the shadowy byways of metaphysical speculation and psychological abstractions – to which research in this direction seems inherently inclined. We also decided early on not to set for ourselves an exclusively anthropic criterion.

But this last proved to be more attractive as a theoretical basis

of research than efficient as a practical means of avoiding error. It is true that a continual reference to human mentality is not the ready highway to truth that it seems at the first glance to be.

There are profound – and to the believer in the theory of continuous mental evolution even startling – differences in the lesser eddies of the psychic stream. The great current is beyond doubt the same in kind, however much it may differ in volume and intensity. But it is of these lesser eddies that the significance becomes obscured by a continual reference to human psychology. This was realised clearly.

On the other hand, outside these differences, the mental processes of the chacma baboons generally are so human-like that it proved impossible to submit them to a critical examination without accepting as a standard our common human experience.

It is necessary to state that the environment of this wild troop was not constituted by conditions which could be described as quite natural.

The troop was completely isolated and had been so apparently for many years, and besides the isolation, the intrusion of man as a dominating element in the environment had also other profound effects in many directions. In the systematic study of behaviour, this in itself would have been an advantage had it been possible to compare habits under such conditions, with those under more natural ones.

But there were two great difficulties in the way of bringing about such a comparison.

The first was the difficulty of finding any troop where man's intrusion had not created habits reactively that would not have existed in his absence.

The second was the supreme difficulty of observing closely and continuously any troop otherwise circumstanced than the one described. We did, however, observe other wild troops under more natural conditions, and the results will be apparent in this record of a small portion of our work.

For this reason, I venture to describe here the most interesting events in their life history.

2

The Distribution of the Baboon

IN THE PREVIOUS CHAPTER I stated that, with the exception of man, the baboon showed a greater divergence from type than can be found in any other animal in South Africa. Not only is there this difference between individuals, but even more noteworthy is the difference among groups, which is of course more definitely regional than the difference between individuals.

Our common grey baboon, known to former investigators as the 'chacma' is found from the Cape Peninsula to a degree of latitude just north of the Limpopo. From there the grey baboon is replaced by the yellow baboon of Rhodesia and the whole of eastern Central Africa.

There are, however, two unique group variations which may be called the south regional division.

In the mountain range which more or less follows the boundary between the Transvaal and Portuguese territory, the green baboon is found. This variation is much rarer than the yellow type. It is found only in the highest mountains, and then only in small troops, and this makes it difficult to obtain specimens. In the less populated areas of Bechuanaland and in portions of the Kalahari the black baboon is found, and at present it has become so scarce that as far as type is concerned, it may be regarded as extinct.

Some investigators classify these variations as true species. In my opinion this is incorrect. There is no doubt that where these kinds adjoin one another they readily cross, and there is no anatomical difference perceptible. Also, among our common grey baboons of the Northern Transvaal, specimens of all these variations are found.

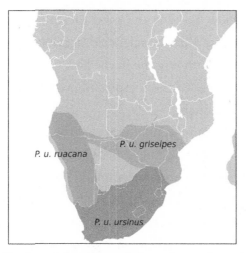

Distribution of the chacma baboon in southern Africa

In Western Central Africa a pure green type is found which also differs anatomically from our baboons.

The colour variations that are found among our grey baboons are definitely restricted to the babies. The colour changes with growth, and the usual grey becomes predominant even before the individual is full grown.

Individual anatomical differences also occur much more frequently in baboons than among any other animal species. The variation among individuals made it possible for us within a short time to know every single one in our tame troop – which could never have happened with any other species of animal.

One has often heard old hunters and also *kaffirs* speak of a short-headed and a long-headed baboon as forming different species, but I was never able to establish the existence of this difference to such a degree. It is true that a great variation in skull formation is found, but I do not believe it is possible to classify two species on this basis.

In connection with the greater degree of variation to be found among the babies, there is an interesting fact which deserves to be mentioned. It is a known scientific fact that the changes which an animal race has undergone in the past make their appearance in many cases again in the foetus and even persist in the infant for a period after birth.

There is, for instance, no doubt that the whale was formerly a four-footed land animal. This is deduced with certainty from the whole skeleton of the huge sea animal. The unborn whale is still a complete four-footed land animal, with the general appearance of some form of pig. Shortly before birth, a general consolidation of the bones takes place which changes the fore-legs into oars and the back legs into the horizontal tail which distinguishes all former land animals from true aquatic animals with a vertical fish-tail. In this way it is often possible to note in the development of the unborn foetus the main great evolutionary stages of a race.

It will possibly surprise most readers to learn that the development of the foetus of our baboon shows a great retrogression: that is to say, if we accept the anthropoid apes and man as the highest point of development that the race of apes has reached. The baboon foetus and the baby baboon prove that the animal is descended from a race which was much more closely allied to the anthropoid apes and man than the full-grown baboon of today.

It is possible to reconstruct the bodily appearance of this ancestor of the baboon from the stages of development of the foetus. The prehistoric baboon was much more erect than his descendant. It was probably more erect even than the present African anthropoid apes. It was clearly a branch of the largest of the existing anthropoid apes, the African gorilla. Our baboon and the gorilla are actually the only true mountain apes which exist today.

But it is not only this characteristic which the baboon has retained. The unique gorilla 'comb', formed by the running together of the eyebrow ridges to make a raised ridge of bone across the back of the skull, has attained a high degree of development in the baboon. The general conformation of the skull of the full-grown baboon is also strongly reminiscent of the gorilla skull.

When, however, we compare the skull of a little baboon with that of a full-grown one, we note at once an enormous variation – in the wrong direction!

Mr Ivy, the well-known Pretoria taxidermist, showed me the skulls of a full-grown and of a young baboon, and from these it appeared clearly that the little one's skull was nearer the human skull than that of the large baboon.

The first peculiarity that could be noticed was the absence of the gorilla 'comb' in the smaller skull.

The reader must remember that this ridge is the most important characteristic differentiating the gorilla skull from that of the human being. From this we would deduce that the absence of the ridge in the little baboon shows a descent from a prehistoric race which possesses a more human-like skull than even the gorilla's. The ridge may be taken as the basis of comparative evolution.

But there are a number of other anatomical proofs.

If we compare, even cursorily, the skull of the little baboon with that of the large one, we note in almost every direction a surprising difference – and all in favour of the little baboon. The round, protruding forehead is considered the most important proof of human likeness in skull formation, and in this respect the little baboon is surprisingly 'human' – much more human than any of the existing anthropoid apes; and the human-likeness of the face and skull is even more noticeable in the unborn baboon than in the fairly developed individual. If we compare its skull with that of an anthropoid ape and man, we must come to the conclusion that our despised baboon comes from a far nobler ancestry than his dog-headedness and quadrupedal form would appear to suggest.

This fact is also established psychologically. The baboon is 'cleverer', and possesses a more human kind of understanding and reason than the investigator would be tempted to conclude from its habits and generally 'unhuman' build. As far as 'understanding' is concerned, there is not at all that great difference between it and the anthropoid apes that most people seem to think there is.

I stated previously that the group variations more definitely distinguishable by reason of colour were also found sometimes among the babies of our grey baboons. I once met with a variation of this kind which was so remarkable that it deserves a detailed account.

An old friend from Waterberg, Commandant Jan Wessels, and I were journeying, shortly after the Anglo-Boer War, to Brandwag on the Palala River. Means of transport were very scarce in those days, and we were compelled to do the journey on horseback. The first night we off-saddled in the mountains to the north of the source of the Palala, and while we were sitting and talking at the fire, we were surprised to hear the clatter of hoofs which were clearly approaching our campfire.

The area was at that time completely uninhabited, and we were at a loss to know what this could be. I think the unveiling of the secret finally increased our astonishment.

Out of the surrounding dark appeared a most wonderful cavalcade. There were about seven or eight young men, all on 'horseback' on oxen, and not the old *kaffir* pack-oxen we knew as children; they were all oxen 'from the span', with saddles and bridles, and the young men were properly 'spurred and armed'. Where they got the rifles and cartridges remains a mystery.

They had come to the *bushveld* to catch young *kwaggas* and ostriches, and at the same time to shoot baboons; for the Milner government at that time had promised to pay ten shillings for every baboon scalp.

The cavalcade was under the leadership of young Frans Lensley, the eldest son of an old well-known Waterberg hunting family.

He too was surprised and pleased to meet me, because with great trouble he had brought with him a little baboon in which he felt sure I would take great interest. It was a baby which he had taken from the mother, which he had shot. He then brought into the firelight a little cardboard shoe box which he had obtained in some *kaffir stad*, and from the shoe box he took out a live baby baboon that he had carefully packed in grass and leaves.

It was the strangest little baboon I have ever seen. My first impression was that it was a little chimpanzee dwarf. The little animal had the round head, the high forehead, and the facial angle of a human being. In every respect the head and face were more human than that of any other baboon or ape I had ever seen.

But there were even stranger and more inexplicable peculiarities. The skin was pitch black – blacker even than the skin of any *kaffir* baby, and the whole body was covered in a pitch black mantle of hair, blacker than the covering of hair of a chimpanzee.

In Europe, I once brought up a baby chimpanzee, so I could compare them. The greatest difference between this little animal and the chimpanzee lay in the hair on the head. The chimpanzee has a path in the middle of the head, and the hair grows smoothly to either side of this parting. This little baboon was different. The hair on the head was smooth towards the front with a veranda-like forelock over the forehead.

Mr Lensley and his companions thought that the animal was a cross between a *kaffir* and a baboon, and there was really much to be said for such a supposition. I was, however, convinced that I had here in my hands an image of the immediate forebear of our baboon.

I would then and there have turned back, had it been possible to get the little baboon home alive, but it soon appeared that its life was in the greatest danger. The previous night it had unexpectedly climbed out of its little box and landed in the fire, with the result that it had burned all four feet very badly. The question of food, too, proved an insoluble difficulty.

Mr Lensley had been able only once to provide food for the strange little captive – when a young native mother had allowed the little baboon to share the source of food of her own infant; from that time – for two days – the baboon had lived on flour-water, which certainly did not help to keep up its vital force.

Notwithstanding all our efforts, the wonderful little creature died that night. I carefully skinned it and cleared and kept every bone of the skull, and the following day Commandant Wessels and I continued our journey.

A few days later, while we were camped for the night, a hyena carried away the skin and bones of the baby baboon from within a yard of my pillow, and although the next day we followed the hyena's spoor for miles, we recovered neither a piece of the skin nor a tuft of hair of perhaps one of the most wonderful little animals that had seen the light of day in South Africa.

3

The Baboons of Doornhoek

OUR FIRST ACQUAINTANCE with the baboons of Doornhoek took place under the most favourable circumstances. Before our arrival, there had been a succession of very good rainy years in Waterberg.

"The wilderness was like Eden and the desert like the garden of the Lord: joy and gladness were found therein", as the prophet aforetime declared, probably under similar circumstances. The beauty and profusion of nature, which every day we had to admire anew, simply cannot be described.

Especially in the mountains of Waterberg, nature exhibited all her treasures. Such a wealth of plants, so many birds of every kind, gathered within such limits I had never before seen equalled, not even in the tropics. As far as insects were concerned it seemed to us that the Egyptian miracle had become manifest before our eyes: that insects were born from the dust of the earth.

This last phenomenon was not always accompanied by admiration, for we had to become intimately acquainted with huge scorpions and spiders which during rainy days made their gruesome appearance from the thatched roofs of our huts.

Snakes of all sorts we met every day, and in the footpath-*kloof* that most dreadful of all reptiles – the black mamba (or *makoppa*, as it is known in Waterberg) often obstructed our path.

Then for the first time, too, we became acquainted with the wild fruit of Waterberg. The mountains were rosy with the many edible berries which here attained a size and had a flavour which made them simply a new fruit for the visitor from the south. Wild peaches, sour *klappers* (unknown in the south) medlars, *moepels*, and various other kinds of fruit made our wilderness a veritable orchard.

It goes without saying that our troop of baboons enjoyed this state of affairs to the full. They were fat and frolicsome, and more beautifully bearded than we ever saw them thereafter. Notwithstanding all this provision, our hard mealies had an irresistible attraction for them.

We little knew when first we settled in Doornhoek that happiness was only on the surface and that the shadow of perpetual tragedy always darkened the lives of these baboons. There was much that we still had to learn.

At night we often heard them wailing and groaning at their sleeping place, but without realising its significance. The wail of a baboon is so 'human' that even hearing it for the first time, one must immediately surmise that it denotes pain and suffering. But we could not be certain of this, and there was no perceptible reason for such lamentation; so that at first we came to the conclusion that the heart-rending sound had probably some cause other than bodily or mental pain, and denoted something other than suffering. But we did not remain in doubt for long.

At that time we kept our horses and vehicles at the farmstead of Mr Willem van Staden, whose house was at the exit of the footpath from the *kloof*; for, of course, no horse or vehicle could come up the *kloof*.

One night Mr Austin and I came back late from Nylstroom, and we had scarcely outspanned [unyoked the horses – *ed.*] when we heard a dreadful noise from the baboons in the *kloof*. For his size, the baboon has probably the loudest voice of any animal on earth. The gruff scream of a full-grown male can be heard just as far as the roar of a lion, and the noise from a large troop in a state of excitement and anger is simply deafening and stunning. It was such a noise we heard that night.

"A leopard has ambushed them early this evening and they are not yet at the sleeping place", was the calm explanation of Mr van Staden. It appeared to us remarkably 'calm', because we had still to climb up that same *kloof,* and the night was unusually dark.

The sight of a leopard was, however, such a common occurrence in the van Staden household, that to have met one was scarcely considered worth mentioning. We were, however, unarmed, and it was absolutely certain that the leopard or leopards were waiting somewhere in the *kloof.* Mr van Staden's suggestion was characteristic. His ten-year-old son would accompany us with a lantern to show us the way, and he would lend both of us the only weapons he had in his house – bayonets fixed to long sticks.

The son said he was quite willing to accompany us, and he would then come home alone the same night. I do not know whether I should be considered as having more than the average degree of cowardice, but I know for certain that I set out on the journey through the *kloof* that night with no great joy. We refused the boy's offer because we felt the danger was too great.

Later the presence of leopards in the *kloof* became so common that we were able to laugh at our erstwhile fears. We soon learnt that there was less danger from an unwounded leopard than from a furious old male baboon.

I walked ahead with the lantern. It became apparent immediately that the whole troop of baboons was gathered on the *kop* on the right-hand and not at their sleeping place in the *krans* on the left-hand side of the *kloof.* The troop was by then fairly tame and knew us well.

The moment the light of our lantern became visible to the troop, there was a sudden silence. The footpath here passed through a stretch of high *tambotie* grass. Just before we passed the boulders, there was a sudden rustle in the grass beside us, and for the wink of an eye, a large leopard was visible in the beam of light.

It crossed the footpath immediately in front of me and disappeared in the heaped-up boulders. This took place so quickly that Mr Austin did not see the leopard. The movement reminded me of a flame which leaps from a large grass fire and vanishes in the air. We learnt then for the first time of the amazing powers of sight in the baboon, which later we established experimentally as being the most acute of any known South African animal.

Notwithstanding the speed of the movement and the darkness of the night, the troop saw the flight of the leopard, and immediately continued the row.

And then a strange thing happened. The leopard was still ahead of us in the *kloof* and unless he had fled up the *kranses*, it was probable that we would meet him again. If we then had the knowledge which we acquired later, we would have known that the behaviour of the baboons could be taken as an infallible guide. If they did not know precisely where the leopard was at that moment, they would never leave their shelter in the dark, and still less would they leave it if they knew there was danger of a second meeting.

While Mr Austin, still flabbergasted, was wondering what we should do under the circumstances, we were suddenly surrounded by the whole troop of baboons, and the noise was bewildering. From all sides, black forms appeared within our circle of light with challenging cries in the direction in which the leopard had disappeared.

We then saw for the first time too that most of the large males were carrying little ones on their backs. We subsequently had the opportunity, on more than one occasion, of seeing the large males carrying the little ones pick-a-back out of danger.

We soon understood the behaviour of the troop that night. It was our first experience of how surprisingly like that of humans their understanding was. They had immediately come to the conclusion that the leopard was afraid of us, and that as long as they stayed near us, they were safe. And that trust was not misplaced. They remained with and around us until we reached the slope of detritus under their sleeping place, and there they left us to take refuge in the safety of their rocky ledge. The last we heard of them were sounds of satisfaction and endearments as mothers found their lost infants in safety again. We did not meet the leopard again that night.

It was not long before we came to realise that the life of the baboon is in fact one continual nightmare of anxiety. During the Boer War the mountain leopards had multiplied just as much and had become just as fearless as the baboons themselves, and before our arrival the slaughter among the troop must have been enormous. According to Mr van Staden, seldom, if ever, did a day pass in which the leopards did not obtain at least one victim. All the baboon's cleverness, all its precautions, all its surprising bravery profited it nought against the sly enemy – an enemy which could make itself completely invisible in a few clumps of grass.

We had many opportunities, not only in our tame troop but also in wild troops in other parts of Waterberg, of viewing from near at hand this ghastly struggle for existence.

Our baboons had two enemies – besides man, of course –

which occupied pride of place in that respect. Of these two types of natural enemy the mountain leopard was by far the most dangerous. This beast of prey embodied virtually, as far as baboons in a large area of Waterberg were concerned, the selective power of nature.

I have used the term 'mountain' leopard, not because I wish to suggest that there is more than one kind of leopard in South Africa, but because the mountain leopard is distinguishable from the type in the level *bushveld* by an unusual development. The leopard that inhabits the mountains becomes much bigger, is stronger, fiercer, and more fearless than the dweller in the bush. Even the honey-bee of the rocky ledges is much fiercer and makes more honey than its like on the flats.

The other enemy that harassed the baboons while we were there was the python, which in that region often attained a length of eighteen feet. It is true that the pythons in our neighbourhood caught far fewer baboons than the leopards. I think this is chiefly due to the fact that the python can be seen more quickly and can, in consequence, rely far less upon surprise in its attack. In order to overcome the baboon, the python also uses exclusively the method of paralysing it by crushing it.

But in one respect the snake enjoyed an unusual advantage over its rival, the leopard. Every living thing has an inborn fear of snakes: in the baboon this fear shows itself in an extreme form. A baboon will attack a leopard. It will always defend itself against a leopard's attack, but in the presence of a snake its bravery sinks to zero.

A troop will never make the least effort to rescue a captured comrade from a python. All the baboons do in such a case is *sauve qui peut*, with an alarm call that makes the mountains echo. And the same troop that is put to cowardly flight by a python will attack the largest and fiercest leopard to save a comrade – that is, in the daylight.

The leopard usually makes use of one special method to catch its prey. It stealthily watches a troop on its way to the sleeping place. Its chosen time is just before sunset. Spying from some high-lying place, it picks out a half-grown baboon which has wandered from the troop, and with all the cunning of its type it chooses an ambush that will bring the baboon within reach of its merciless claws. No matter how acute the baboon's power of vision, the mantle of invisibility which the leopard seems to possess plays the fool with even the baboon's astonishing keen-sightedness.

The leopard waits until its prey is well within its reach, and then with a flame-like movement it strikes its unrelenting claws into the baboon, and before the baboon can think of flight or defence, the leopard has it. It bites in one of two places only – either in the neck, or on the spine in the small of the back. In the first case death follows immediately – often even before the victim has had a chance of making its death-cry audible to its mates. But in most cases I have personally witnessed, the spine was chosen as the wounding place. And it is just this which makes the capture of a baboon (where it happens towards dark) such a ghastly tragedy for the human spectator or auditor.

When the leopard bites in the spine, an immediate and incurable paralysis of the hind quarters follows. But in whatever way the attack occurs – whether the leopard kills outright or only paralyses – its behaviour after the attack is always the same.

It flees immediately with the greatest speed to some shelter where it will be perfectly protected from attack by baboons. A deep slit in the rocks, a cliff-cave with a narrow entrance, or even the point of a high branch are the most favoured spots. Whichever of these it be, however, the place is always so chosen that the baboons can reach the leopard only from the front, and then not more than one at a time. In such circumstances the leopard is quite safe, and the baboons never venture to attack. But the leopard's flight follows of necessity, for as soon as knowledge of the murder reaches the troop, all the large males storm with the greatest anger and bravery towards the enemy, and woe betide the leopard if it falls into their hands before it has reached its shelter.

On one occasion I witnessed in broad daylight the hate (and the accompanying bravery) of the baboon for the leopard. Mr Dolf Snyder was cutting poles in one of the *kloofs* of the Hangklip mountains where I was spending a few days with him. At the time we were at the top of a narrow *kloof* which ended in a basin of *kranses*. On the highest *krans* we saw a troop of baboons obviously in a state of extreme excitement.

For some time we could not discover the cause, although from the kind of noise they were making, I guessed at the presence of a leopard. And finally, we saw a large male leopard creeping on a ledge against the face of the *krans*. Directly above him were the baboons, but so far above him that there was no chance of an attack. We could see the animal was making its way to the entrance of the cave in the *krans* at the end of the ledge. But long before it reached its haven of refuge, the distance between the two *kranses* narrowed so much that the leopard had to pass no more than twelve feet below the baboons. And here two large males awaited it.

As I well remember, what then happened was greeted with

exclamations of surprise and encouragement from both of us. Just as the leopard passed immediately below the two baboons, they cast themselves without hesitation to the depth below and both landed on the tyrant. There was a moment of confused struggling. Then we saw the leopard, as is its habit, lying on its back with one baboon between its forepaws, while the other gripped it from behind and prevented it from also using its hind claws. The first baboon, however, had the leopard by the throat, so that from the start the leopard could not use its teeth.

The struggle was short. The great eye-teeth of the baboon soon did their work, and within a few minutes the huge leopard was motionless under the baboons. But the first hero had sacrificed his life in the attack. On both flanks, the claws of the leopard had exposed the lungs, and the baboon struggled only a few yards away from its enemy before it too died on the ledge.

I think we took no little share in the rejoicing with which the troop greeted the fall of their arch-enemy.

With much trouble, we later obtained the body of the leopard, and then we saw that on one hind leg it bore fresh wounds from a trap, and this also gave evidence of the power of vision of the baboons.

4
Birth Pain in Man and Animal

IMMEDIATELY after birth, the little baboon is placed before its mother's breast where it clings with all four 'hands' to the long hair which clearly has undergone a special development for this purpose. As long as the mother is moving, the baby must bear the whole weight of its body itself without assistance from the mother, who must naturally use all four feet for walking. As soon as the mother stops, she immediately takes up an erect position, and the baby then has the support of the lower portion of her body. Often she places one arm round her baby, probably to give its little arms a rest while it is sitting still.

It always surprised visitors to see how newly-born helpless babies, that could not yet move of their own accord when on the ground, could carry not only the weight of their own bodies, but could bear, without ever falling off, the heavy shaking and bumping caused by the unavoidable movements of the mother. This power is of course, common to all apes. Even man has retained this ability among other similar useless ape-likenesses which still exist within our species.

On various occasions, I have shown to persons interested that a human baby half an hour old often clings in the same way immediately when it is placed in contact with a hairy *kaross* (a skin blanket). Even the little toes curl inwards in an effort to get a grip with them too. But in this respect, man's evolution has left him in the lurch. The human baby can curl his feet inwards very much farther than a full-grown person can – as the well-known law of evolution would lead us to expect – but he can no longer grip with the foot. With his hands, however, the newly born

human infant can clutch the hair of the *kaross* so firmly that it can not only be picked up hanging from the *kaross* but can stand a fair amount of bumping and shaking. A human infant of an hour old can hang thus for twenty minutes to the hair of a *kaross*, or even from a walking-stick, without any signs of fatigue, but the experiment is usually accompanied by a terrific screaming, whereby the baby apparently wishes to convey that it no longer finds this mode of conveyance desirable.

Later on, when her little one is so big that it can walk about for short distances, the mother baboon begins to carry it on her back. This makes it much easier for her to move about. While the baby is still small it is carried high up the back where it is perched like a human baby with outstretched arms and legs flat against its mother's body. As its weight increases, it sits more and more erect on its mother's back and moves progressively backwards until, when it is fairly large, it sits upright on the mother's hips, where its weight hinders her least.

In no other respect is the 'communism' of the baboon so clearly seen as in the treatment of the babies of the troop. As long as the baby is very small, its father and mother pay it exclusive attention. No other individual in the troop will touch it – except perhaps the little brother or sister which immediately preceded it. It amused us a great deal to see the curiosity and surprise of the older brother or sister when the little new-comer appeared on the scene. Carefully it would touch the new baby all over, smell it, pull open its eyes and mouth, search through its downy hair and examine it outside and inside (as far as that was possible) from head to foot. It was only from her own young that the mother permitted such liberties.

As soon as the little one can walk, it is handled and fondled by all the large members of the troop. There is often great rivalry among the medium-sized ones to get hold of such a new member of the community for the first time and to fondle it. When an opportunity occurs a small company gathers together and the new baby is then handed from one to the other until all have made acquaintance with it. The behaviour of the mother on such occasions is ridiculously human. She sits on one side and it is clear that she makes every effort to appear unconcerned. Nevertheless her mother's pride beams from her every movement and gesture. It is almost as if you can hear her murmur to herself, "Yes, have a good look, you have never seen such a baby before..."

When the troop is in danger, the baboon exhibits, in the protection of the little ones, its highest degree of altruism. The large males will, with the greatest courage, sacrifice their lives – even with recklessness – in an effort to save the little ones. Never was our troop so dangerous – even towards us – as when a little one, for some reason or other, took fright and gave a cry of alarm.

When that happened, we were sometimes in real danger, and it was for this reason alone that during our association with the troop, we were usually armed with revolvers.

I mentioned the surprise the older brothers and sisters showed at the first sight of their new relative. That was because the arrival is always a surprise to them, due to the circumstances under which birth takes place, *i.e.* always under the most secret conditions the father and mother can arrange. No other baboon – far less a human being – is allowed even in the neighbourhood.

Near the sleeping place there was, in a corner of the rocks, a large *gwarrie* bush which could be approached from one side only, and in it most of the births among the troop took place. We experienced the greatest difficulty in getting a view of the event. The best we could ever manage was to watch it with binoculars from a suitable *kop*, and even then it was only from a glimpse now and then that we could reconstruct the course of events.

We could always fix the time of the event by the fact that the mother and father separated themselves from the troop. In most cases they remained near the sleeping place in the morning, when the rest of the troop went out for its daily search for food. The whole troop respected the birth laws. No matter how curious the baboon may be, we never saw an attempt by either old or young to disturb the mother by watching. In fact the troop always carefully removed itself from the place.

Once we saw a few of the eleven leaders come unexpectedly, and clearly unwillingly, upon a birth. In this instance it was a young pair, and it was their first infant that would shortly see the light of day. It was obvious that the young mother was taken unawares by the event and she had scarcely had time to separate herself from the troop before she was in the pangs of labour. The place in which this couple took refuge was a narrow passage along which the troop had to trek; and if they were not disposed to make a long and difficult detour, they would have to pass in the immediate neighbourhood of the young mother. The young male stood on guard in a state of great excitement at the entrance to the passage while from afar we could hear the groaning of the wife in her hiding place. Every few minutes the husband would hurry back, probably to help her. The behaviour of the male was always the same in such cases, but we were never able actually to see what he did. But from the observation of many instances we could deduce with some certainty that he is of assistance to her in various ways.

To return to the instance under consideration. The troop was led on this morning by about six of the eleven leaders. The young pair had hastened far ahead when the young female had become aware of her first pains, with the result that the leaders came upon them when the birth was already somewhat advanced.

In the narrow entrance to the passage the young male stood in threatening attitude. Under ordinary circumstances, he would never have dared to show the least resistance towards a single one of the leaders; and the leaders, on the other hand, if such a thing had happened, would simply have crushed the foolhardy one. The baboon 'leader' is a relentless tyrant in the maintenance of his supremacy over the troop.

In this instance, the behaviour of the leaders surprised us. As soon as they heard the groaning of the young female and saw the male on guard in the passage, they called a halt and took counsel. It is on such occasions that the spectator so strongly gets the feeling that the baboon can really talk.

If you learn to know them, you realise more and more that the baboon leader seldom or never acts or makes a noise without a definite purpose. Here the troop slowly gathered into a clump around the six leaders in front while all watched the young male with great interest and listened to the noises made by the female. It was clearly a surprise to all of them, and here was a problem that had to be solved at once. The only other route for the troop was long and very difficult, and one moreover which, within our knowledge, the troop had never used before. Among the older ones there was a hushed 'talking' and 'whispering', coupled with hesitant movements.

It was all so completely human that it was impossible not to form the impression that, deeply impressed by this unexpected happening, they became wise and authoritative old gentlemen, busy discussing the matter from all angles. There was no pointless excitement. Even the young ones sat down quietly in the background – albeit with neck-stretching curiosity. And the result certainly helped to strengthen the impression that baboons could talk. Suddenly the members of the council came to a decision – with one accord, they turned around and chased the remainder of the troop along the road they had come. Some of the more curious ones were driven back by the old members with bellowed threats and the young pair were left in peace in their seclusion. The troop followed the difficult detour, climbed up a *krans*, and wasted at least two hours just to avoid the place of birth.

All the births we had the opportunity of watching took place, as far as the behaviour of the female, the male, and the troop were concerned, in more or less the same way.

I mentioned the groaning of the female and the pain which obviously she suffers. We finally learnt to know the baboons well enough to be able to distinguish all the noises they usually made.

There was no possibility of making a mistake about the sounds which denoted pain and suffering.

We soon established that in all nature known to us, there was no other animal which underwent greater birth pain than the baboon: and this lead me to a most interesting discovery. As far as I know, the mystery of birth pain has never yet been explained satisfactorily from a psychological point of view. Why must the most important experience in animal life be coupled with pain and suffering – a fact which must serve to make it something undesirable in the life of higher animals, while we would expect that natural selection would have had the tendency, as in the case of everything which can serve to ensure the survival of individuals and the race, to make such an event more attractive and less dangerous?

In man, birth pain reaches its highest degree. Birth – the most important and most 'natural' event in the history of the individual and of the race – is ranked among the most important surgical operations in man, and in our day seldom takes place without the administration of chloroform. In many cases, it endangers the life of the mother as well as of the child. Anything more 'unnatural', anything more in conflict with all the laws of natural selection is hardly conceivable.

One important principle in connection with birth pain has certainly long since been discovered by investigators, although I must admit I have never met with an exposition of it. This principle is that throughout organic nature birth pain is coupled with the care of the young. Where there is no care of the young, there is no noticeable sign of birth pain. (The laying of eggs is classified for my purposes as birth.)

A second great principle is that all important 'soul states' or 'soul movements' in the organic world are started by a psychological 'key'. It would take too long and would remove me too far from my subject to discuss this aspect of the matter fully.

To make it clear, I shall mention only the bringing into action of the sexual sense. It occurs in three different ways in nature: either scent or colour or sound, and sometimes by a mixture of two or all of these 'keys'. The sexual sense of most mammals can never come into operation or be aroused without the necessary scent which appears for this purpose at the appropriate time.

With these two great principles in mind, it is not difficult to arrive at a theoretical solution of the whole problem.

Let us return for a moment to the connection between care of the young and birth pain.

Pain is such an important and outstanding phenomenon in nature that it is easy to distinguish the signs which denote it in all organisms. It is something so common and so fundamental that all expressions of pain have, as it were, a common factor. As far as life is concerned, pain is the angel with the flaming sword who guards the way to death. If pain vanished from the organic world, everything animal on earth would vanish too within a few generations.

Consider first the lowest stages of animal life. There are many insects that show not the least sign of care for their young and never even see them. In all such cases the laying of eggs takes place with the greatest ease and without the least sign of pain. The scorpion is one of the exceptional insects which brings its young into the world alive. The young are born in pairs, and here there can be no doubt that the process is accompanied by a great deal of pain. As soon as they are born the mother takes them carefully with her dangerous pincers and places them on her back where, like the young baboons, they cling. They are cared for by the mother, guarded against dangers, and fed until they are large enough to fend for themselves.

In our antelopes it can clearly be seen from their behaviour that the immediate result of birth pain is to fix the attention of the mother on her newly born little one.

Birth pain is, just as scent in the case of the sexual sense, the key that awakens the psychological impetus of mother love. The two go hand in hand and are always commensurate with each other.

In this connection, I undertook the interesting and more or less corroborative experiment. The small self-coloured goats were known to be free of the general goat weakness of 'throwing away' their young. I placed several ewes, for a period, before and after birth under the influence of chloroform. In those cases where the mother felt no birth pain, she refused to recognise or take her infant. In cases where the mother was made insensible after the birth pain commenced, the acceptance and refusal of the kids was about equal.

In my opinion there are enough facts to justify my theory that birth pain is the natural key that brings into existence the psychological state of mother love. By the destruction of natural selection in man, this result shows the same divergence from type that is observable in the workings of the sexual sense.

In the baboon mother love reaches a higher stage of development than in any other animal in our country, and the birth pain she suffers is proportionate to it.

5
Behaviour and Character
of Young Baboons

AS FAR AS general behaviour is concerned, possibly a greater difference is observable between that of little ones and of full-grown specimens than in any other species of animal. All small animals are naturally more disposed to play than old ones of the same species. But in the baboon the difference goes much deeper, and seems sometimes to touch the very foundations of character and behaviour.

Three-quarters of the life of the baboon is spent in play. Conditions which produced states of the greatest despondency and sadness among the old ones of our troop never entirely kept the young ones from their play. There is no doubt that states of sorrow did affect them also, but it was noticeable only through a lessened noisiness.

As soon as the baboon is full grown, it appears to become morose and capricious. All the happiness and playfulness of its childhood days deserts it. The pressure of life seems to overshadow its spirit more and more. The search for food and self-protection against the countless dangers which threaten it from all sides seem to absorb all its attention, and the only occasions on which the better side of its nature is brought out is in its association with the little ones of the troop. As I mentioned before, it then exhibits a surprising degree of unselfishness and love, even towards the young of other animals.

When we had come to know the members of our troop, we noticed that there was a surprising difference of character between individuals. In this respect, there is no other animal which the baboon resembles so much as man.

Some are reserved, quiet, often capricious and inclined to withdraw from the communal life of the troop. The extreme limit of this type of character is the one which is always in a bad humour, and that allows itself to get into a state of extreme anger from some trifling cause. It is malicious, and is constantly suppressing the young ones around it, often for behaviour which seems to waken interest in the other old members of the troop. Often such an individual is greatly disturbed by the noise that the little ones make during their pranks. It charges at them, 'cursing' as though the heavens had fallen, and alas for the little one it gets hold of. Frequently we saw a few of the leaders rescue such a little one by force from the cross-grained old male who was always prone to punish heavily and without reason.

The opposite limit of this trait among the baboons is the good-natured unselfish type, ready to tolerate anything from the youngsters, and often ready to take part with them in their fun. It was noticeable how soon even the smallest recognised these kind-hearted ones, and put their patience to the test.

At evening time, when the troop had gathered on the rocky edges of the mountain stream, from all sides the little ones would leave their mothers to make an attack on such an old one. From in front and from behind they climbed over him and with their little milk teeth tried to bite his scarred skin through the matted hair. There seemed to be no limit to his patience. He often pretended he had been overcome, fell over backwards, and tried unavailingly to free himself from his attackers. In this respect he was an excellent actor. He showed all the signs of extreme fear and helplessness, but even then he would never handle a single one of the little ones except with the utmost gentleness. Now and again one of the larger youngsters, when it could no longer resist the temptation, would join in the attack, and in such cases the human-like playfulness of the baboon appeared in a remarkable fashion. Several times we saw the old baboon, troubled too much and bitten too sharply by a somewhat malicious half-grown one, take the youngster by the scruff of its neck, walk slowly to the bank of a stone-basin pool with it, and duck it head and feet.

The little ones of our troop were particularly attached to three different games.

In the *kloof*, immediately below the sleeping place, there was a large wild fig tree that grew aslant over a pool. The tree had a single stem about thirty feet long which was so flexible that it made an excellent swing for the little ones: and for this purpose they used it. The tree must have served as a swing for generations because the bark was polished as smooth as a mirror, and only at the upper end were a few green branches allowed to grow. On this stem the young baboons learnt all sorts of surprising gymnastic feats.

The commonest game was 'follow-my-leader' (a favourite with human children). A row of little baboons would climb the stem from the base and set it swinging by rhythmically swaying up and down; then from the topmost, one after the other would let go to be thrown through the air in all directions to land on the tops of tree ferns or the edges of the rocks that surrounded the pool. We never saw one fall into the water, although there was great danger that this might happen. It was, moreover, a usual prank for the penultimate one in the row to grab the topmost by the tail just as it was about to let go for its flight through the air. It was, naturally, an attempt to jerk the caught one into the water. But he was always too quick for that to succeed.

The beautiful rocky pool just below the sleeping place always gave pleasure to the babies. Here the troop enjoyed their evening drink before they went to their sleeping place, and it was the custom, especially of the little ones, to hold their tiny faces against the surface of the water and for hours at a time to admire (as Narcissus of old) their own beauty in the natural mirror. Many of them learnt to put their noses just below the surface and to blow bubbles which they then tried to catch in their hands. There too they played an old-fashioned trick on one another. While one youngster was completely absorbed in the contemplation of his own image, another from outside would quietly stalk his mate and jump suddenly and hard on his back. The result was always that the first-mentioned fell into the water. But occasionally – so quick and lithe is the little baboon – the one attacked was lucky enough, despite the surprise and fright, to catch hold of his attacker and pull him also into the water.

Another game took place in a large tree fern in the *kloof*. The stem was so smooth that it was very difficult for even the little baboons to reach the crown. The top of the tree had been so flattened that there was a surface of only a few inches in diameter on which they could sit. The game consisted in taking possession of the little seat and preventing any other baboon from getting on to it. We often wondered how it was possible for this game not to end in serious accidents, because the little baboons romped wildly on the tree fern top, and there was a possible drop of twenty feet.

This reckless playing of the babies reminds me of another instance which Commandant Wessels and I watched with unabated interest every day for weeks in another troop.

It was in the *veld* between the Palala and the Magalakwen. That northern area was quite uninhabited, and such names of farms as we knew were merely the names given by old hunters who had formerly shot elephants there. Sandmansfontein was one of the old camping grounds where Commandant Wessels and I camped one winter. It was a circular basin surrounded by steep cliffs and approachable from only one *poort* (mountain pass). On the east side of the basin there was a *krans* quite a thousand feet high and a mile long. This *krans* hung over so far that when the sun was directly overhead, there was a shadow of at least twenty feet wide at its base. There was no mountain animal, including the baboon, that could climb such a rock face; and yet the baboons made a surprising use of the *krans*.

We had camped a few hundred feet from the base of the *krans* so that we had a view of its whole length. In this basin there was a troop of about two hundred baboons. For generations, certainly, they had not come in contact with human beings as enemies, because the only sign of human beings we found dated from the days of the old elephant-hunters. There were, for instance, a series of traps still so efficient that one of our natives was caught, horse and all, on the first day we were there.

On our first visit to Sandmansfontein, there were many leopards constantly on the watch to catch baboons, and the smallness of the troop must certainly be ascribed to the activities of this beast of prey. The baboons, however, had discovered a fortress which protected them, at least at night, against all attacks from their arch-enemy.

The *krans* ended on the right-hand side in a solitary *kop* in which there was a cave. This cave was the sleeping place of the troop and they took care that every evening they got back to it by twilight. The only entrance to the cave was along the face of the *krans*, and at first sight one would come to the conclusion that no animal without wings could ever reach it.

But under pressure of deadly danger, the baboons had found a way. About the middle of the *krans* face and at least 500 feet from the base, there was a narrow ledge that stretched the whole length of the *krans*. The ledge was nowhere more than probably a few inches wide – at least so it appeared to us through binoculars. Along this terrifying way the baboons travelled every morning and every evening from and to the cave, and on every occasion we watched the awful spectacle from below with bated breath.

Human emotions operate in a strange way. Commandant Wessels and I had shot many baboons. There was every reason for hating and despising the destroyer, and under ordinary circumstances we would never have deplored the death of a baboon. None the less, we were petrified as we watched the daily journey of the baboons along the gigantic *krans* face. I am certain that it would have profoundly shocked us to see one drop. During our stay, however, this never happened.

There was only one way in which the baboons could travel this dizzy road. They had to go more than a mile hanging only by their fingers to the ledge; their hind feet against the smooth surface of the *krans*. There was no other support for hand or foot except the narrow ledge – and below, a fall of 500 feet. The procession always performed the journey in one set way. In the van were the large males, then followed the females without babies, then the females with babies on their backs, and in the rear came the youngsters already separated from their mothers.

It was a sight to make one shudder. The journey of the mothers with fairly large babies on their backs appeared to us particularly hazardous. Through the binoculars it often appeared to us that some could not possibly carry the overhanging weight – and here and there were spots where all had to pass round some projecting point in the *krans*. The baboons themselves saw the danger because at such places they moved very slowly and with the utmost caution. A troop of baboons is seldom, if ever, quiet. It seems as though they experience a special pleasure in making a noise. But this journey was always completed in deathly silence, and I am sure this helped to make the spectacle more impressive for us.

Our emotions can be judged from this: on several occasions the suggestion was made that a shot be fired at the baboons just when they had reached the most dangerous point in the *krans* road, but it remained a suggestion – neither of us had the heart to fetch a gun.

And I have not yet told the most awful part of this spectacle. Even here – amidst the most terrible danger – the young baboons could not give up their pranks, even for a few moments. One of their favourite games was for a young baboon to free one hand from the ledge and while swinging from the other above the awful precipice, catch a mate by the tail and give a sharp jerk. It often appeared to us that it was but a matter of a hair's breadth between safety and a crash into the depths below for both youngsters. But we probably over-estimated the danger, and the baboons had gauged it more correctly. In any case, we never saw one fall.

A strange peculiarity in the character of young baboons is the love they show for everything small. Those that we kept at the homestead had each a little animal to which it was so attached that when a separation had to take place, as was unavoidable on a farm, it always ended in a tragedy. Little goats and lambs, piglets and puppies, kittens, even chickens, ducklings, and goslings had all been noted by us as the favourite playmates of little baboons which grew up at the homestead. This attraction is, of course, similar to that which all small animals have for the human child. Our little baboons, however, never showed any interest in dolls or imitation animals. All such were immediately broken – 'to see what's inside'.

In Europe I kept for some years a little ape – a South American marmoset, which belongs to the smallest species of ape in the world. This ape was so small that it could easily creep into my waistcoat pocket. It was certainly no larger than a field-mouse. For her size and development, she was, however, remarkably clever. A young lady who had cared for her for a time during my absence had given her a little doll of which she was at first afraid, but when she discovered that the doll was not alive, she immediately accepted it as a plaything. It was funny to see what fondling the doll received. The ape never went to sleep without taking the doll in her arms. This is the only ape, in my experience, that showed the least interest in playthings or imitation animals.

What always surprised me, in comparison with the great interest which the baboons at the homestead displayed in young animals, was that our troop in the mountains seldom made any attempt to get hold of little mountain animals, although there was ample opportunity to do so. The troop most often have had the chance of catching little klipbuck, dassies, and red hares, and yet, with one exception, this never occurred. Of the dassies the baboons simply took no notice – almost as little as the dassies found anything in the baboons to disturb them. On a few occasions we saw one of the troop frightening dassies asleep in the sun by suddenly jumping between them from a height above them. Two other males had the habit, when the opportunity occurred, of throwing stones and rubble at the dassies, but we never saw an attempt to catch a dassie.

The first time I heard of the capture of a little animal by baboons was when Dr. Zboril told me about it. Dr Zboril was a mining engineer by profession and on one occasion in the Zoutpansberg *low-veld*, his native servants told him about a troop of baboons in the mountains that years before had captured near their *stad* and brought up a goat kid.

According to their report, the goat was at that time still with the troop. After a great deal of trouble Dr Zboril caught sight of the troop, and took several photos of this unique event, one of which he showed to me.

The captive was by then a full-grown pure white goat ram with a long beard and horns, and it was always among the troop. The natives said that often three or four young baboons rode on the back of the large ram, but Dr Zboril never saw this himself. But it is nevertheless highly probable, if one remembers how soon young baboons at the farm learn by themselves to ride on dogs, pigs, and other tame animals.

It is obvious that there are few animals that would be able to remain with the troop of baboons during their daily journeys in the mountains, so that the chance of rearing a captive animal is small and would be limited to only a few kinds. It is also improbable that baboons possess sufficient intelligence to provide a young animal with a foster-mother when the captive is still too small to fend for itself. It may possibly happen when a female of the troop has in some way lost her newly born infant just at the time of the capture of the foreign little animal. But this is a fortuitous concatenation of circumstances which can rarely happen. It is highly probable that Dr Zboril's little goat was caught after it was large enough to do without its mother.

The *kaffirs*, however, declared that at first the little goat was carried about by a female baboon in her arms. It is therefore possible (but only just possible) that a female baboon, having lost her own child, took the goat as a foster-child. In such a case she would carry it in her arms and even take the trouble to teach it to suckle from her. Usually goat kids can easily be taught to take to other animals as foster-mothers.

I mentioned one exception in our troop of the absence of attempts to catch small animals. This exception appeared so strange to us that we studied the event carefully from beginning to end.

One afternoon as the troop returned, we noticed that they were in a state of excitement – and this was visible when they were still a considerable distance from the *kloof*. They would constantly gather into a heap around something which clearly aroused their interest. We went to meet them, and then discovered that the unusual behaviour was due to a small newly born rock-hare that a young female had in her arms. As in all other species of hare, the rock-hare mother has the habit of leaving her young at the lair while she goes to graze. This happens mostly at night, but also occurs during the day. I think it is a form of protection that makes the mother fashion a lair for herself some distance from her young, while she visits them only periodically when they must be fed. It was probably such a solitary little hare that the female baboon discovered, and of which she immediately took possession.

All the members of the troop took the greatest interest in the little captive, and made constant efforts to touch it, but the possessor warded off all such attempts. The right of possession is one of the tribal laws most rigidly respected by baboons, so that there was no danger that one of the larger ones would actually attempt to take away the hare from the female by force. We knew that by then.

But the female was more suspicious of us. What her companions would or would not do she knew well enough, but what human beings would do in such a case was another matter. She consequently took the safest course, and kept her hare at a safe distance from us and nothing we could offer her was a great enough temptation to make her come within our reach.

We saw at once that the hare was much too small and helpless to feed itself, so that an unhappy end to the experiment was a certainty unless we could devise some means of feeding it. We were certainly more anxious than even the baboons to keep the hare alive to see what would happen afterwards, but that was exactly what the young owner would not allow us to do. All kinds of titbits were offered to her in vain. These only seemed to accentuate her suspicions about our intentions. We even tried, with the help of our natives, to catch her in a trap, but she was much too clever for that.

We might have had an opportunity of getting hold of the hare at night to feed it, but for some reason which we never discovered, our troop would never allow us to get on to the sleeping place at night. While they were still in the *kloof,* we could get into the closest contact with them, but once they were in their sleeping place we could never approach nearer than the branches of the wild fig tree that served as the entrance. From there we could see everything that happened in the sleeping place, but as soon as one of us placed a foot on the floor, he was threatened by the large males in a manner that left us in no doubt as to their intentions. So we never dared to climb on to the floor of the sleeping place while the troop was there.

The young female slept with the hare in her arms, and not for a moment was the little animal allowed out of her possession. This naturally hindered her own search for food, and usually she was left far behind while the troop was journeying. She usually carried the hare under one arm and walked on three legs. When she found something to eat, she held the hare between her back legs while she used both her hands.

This went on for three days. We left little dishes of milk in the *kloof* and on the floor of the sleeping place in the hope that the hare would perhaps be allowed to drink from them. The milk was, however, immediately accepted as a special present to the leaders, and even the young baboons did not dare to approach the dishes until the leaders had emptied them completely.

We could see the weakness of the hare increasing daily, and on the third night of its captivity, it died on the sleeping place. During the night it was thrown out and the following morning we found its body on the brink of the rock pool immediately below the sleeping place. We ascertained that it had died of hunger.

It is noteworthy that the young female mourned the loss of her hare for several days. Every evening, she separated herself from the troop and, perched on the top of some pointed rock, she gave vent to her sorrow with the sounds of baboon lamentation. This she kept up *ad nauseam*.

Except for the capture of the rock hare, we never saw a similar event among our troop. But on various occasions we saw examples of friendship between baboons and other animals. The strangest example I ever personally saw happened in the neighbourhood of Bokpoort. It was coupled with a number of unusual events, and even if some of them have nothing to do directly with baboons, they nonetheless led to the discovery of the incident, so I shall tell the story in detail.

6
Friendship Between
Men and Baboons

THE AFFECTION which baboons often show towards small animals extends sometimes to human babies. In this respect I refer, of course, only to tame baboons in captivity. Several cases came to our notice in which tame baboons had developed unusual attachment for human babies, and one even in which a baby had been entrusted by its mother to the care of a young baboon.

This occurred on the farm. At that time we had little tame baboons which were free to roam about the homestead. The wife of a *bywoner* (A squatter, or poor white tenant) on the farm washed clothes once a week in our dam. She used to bring with her her little baby in a handcart she had made out of a soap box and four plough wheels. While she worked, the baby was left in the shade of a tree. One little baboon immediately took great interest in the baby.

At first the mother forcibly warded off these attentions, but the largest of our young baboons was too clever for her. With the utmost cunning, it would creep up to the baby and on several occasions it circumvented the mother's watchfulness with the result that sometimes she found the baboon in the cart with its arms folded around the child.

In time she became accustomed to this association. She even noticed that when the baby was troublesome, the presence of the baboon soon soothed the child. The result was that instead of frightening the baboon away, she often called in its aid to comfort the child to sleep.

In Waterberg, cases occurred in which full-grown tame baboons showed the same interest in babies, and in one of which the consequences were much more serious and might easily have had fatal results.

On the farm Slypsteenkop, between Warmbaths and Rooiberg, there was a large male baboon tied to a pole in the farmyard. The lady of the house had given birth to a baby which the father, when the child was a few weeks old, showed to the baboon without, however, allowing it to touch the child. The baboon immediately displayed the greatest interest in the baby and thereafter always greeted its appearance with the usual sounds of affection which baboons also make when they beg for anything. The baboon discovered that if it stood upright in its sleeping box, it could catch a glimpse of the baby through the bedroom window. It acquired the habit of climbing every few minutes on to its sleeping box to spy on the child where it lay sleeping in the bedroom. This became a joke at which the household often laughed, and it was pointed out to visitors as a unique baboon trick.

On one occasion, when the husband was away and there was not a single man at the homestead, the baboon broke its chain. The mother and a native maid were busy in the kitchen and they first became aware of something amiss when they heard the baby crying violently. When they rushed into the bedroom, the baboon was sitting on the window-sill with the baby in its arms while with bared teeth it threatened the two intruders.

Without hesitation the mother rushed forward to save her child. The baboon was unusually large and strong, and in all probability it would have been able to retain its booty by force, in spite of anything the two women could do. But it decided to adopt another course. Just outside the window there was a thick creeper, the highest branches of which reached the roof and up this, with the baby in its arms, the baboon scrambled. In a few seconds it was, as far as the efforts of the mother were concerned, safe on the ridge of the roof.

Desperate and almost beside herself, the unfortunate mother had to watch from below. She soon realised that the greatest danger lay in the fact that the baboon might now suddenly let the baby drop, which would naturally have meant certain death to the child. Every effort was made to entice the baboon down again. Bread, biscuits, sugar, plates of preserve were offered to it, but all to no purpose. Sweets, which it usually attacked eagerly and greedily, had lost all their power of attraction.

The baboon, of course, soon saw through the mother's plan and at all costs it wanted to prevent its being carried out. Instead of climbing down, it began to have doubts about the safety of its position on the ridge of the roof. Alongside the gable of the house there was an indigenous tree – a giant, with wide-stretched branches, one of which was within reach of the baboon. It was soon in the tree and took up a position with the baby on the highest attainable branch, some sixty feet from the ground. For most of the time it carried the child under one arm, sometimes head downwards, but when it was safe on the branch it took the baby in both arms again and then for the first time the crying of the child suddenly ceased. The swaying of the tree, coupled with the warmth of the baboon's body, had sent the little one to sleep.

In the meantime, the mother had sent the maid to the nearest neighbour for help. However, someone in the neighbourhood had heard the calling and screaming of the woman, and had speedily come to help. But it soon appeared that the man who arrived was as helpless as the woman. The only suggestion he could offer was to shoot the baboon dead and catch the baby as it fell – but this plan was provisionally set aside as an extreme measure which could not be used as long as the child was not in greater danger. All that the man and the mother could do was to stand under the tree immediately below the baboon, and unremittingly hold out an outstretched blanket.

An hour later the maid returned with a Bushman who had formerly worked on Slypsteenkop, and who had been a great friend of the baboon.

It is a well-known fact that many Bushmen have the ability to get on friendly terms very quickly with animals. Such an intimacy had once existed between the baboon of Slypsteenkop and this Bushman, and it appeared that the baboon had not forgotten its friend. The Bushman put the sweets aside. He was of the opinion that they would only serve to keep the animal's suspicions alive.

He made the man, the mother, and the maid go into the house and close all the doors and windows. Then he began to talk to the baboon in the language and in the manner which Bushmen use with baboons. This immediately touched some chord in the baboon's brain and without the least mistrust it climbed down the tree with the baby under its arm and allowed the Bushman to get hold of it by the collar.

When it was again attached to its chain, all its courage deserted it. Without any protest it handed the baby to the Bushman and the mother recovered her child without any serious consequences except a few scratches on its hands and face from the branches of the tree. The baboon paid with its life for this escapade.

Another case in which wild baboons were in friendly association with human beings I saw personally at the entrance

PHOTO: DR LISA SHARE

Researcher and biologist Professor Robert Sapolsky and friend

to Bokpoort in the Hanglip mountains. I was in the company of two old Waterbergers when we unexpectedly came upon the scene. One of the two, Mr Willem van Staden, was already well into his seventies, and Mr Gys van Rooyen was just seventy. Both were virtually born in the hunting-*veld* and had grown up among wild animals. But to both these old gentlemen the sight was a surprise and filled them with wonderment. Never before had they experienced, or even heard, of anything like it.

It is remarkable that the taming of our troop of baboons in Doornhoek caused no surprise among the old inhabitants of the *veld*. They could easily understand how we had brought about such a state of affairs by the methods we adopted. It was rather affairs that awoke the deepest suspicion.

But the Bokpoort incident was a challenge to the mental stability of the authors; one that made all their previous knowledge and experience of animal behaviour totter.

It was something I had never experienced before. The sight is fixed in my memory by a series of singular events which in certain respects were as surprising as the incident itself, and to which they were closely related. Notwithstanding the digression, I have decided to tell the whole history shortly. It will at least give the reader a livelier picture of the natural surroundings in which we came upon this incident.

At that time there were two roads that gave access from our side of the Hanglip mountain to the Palala plateau and the farm Purekrans. The one was the large wagon road through Tarantaalstraat – almost a day's detour for us. The other was through Bokpoort.

There was no made road through Bokpoort. That came many years later. The only road was a footpath – both difficult and somewhat dangerous. Of course, no vehicle of any sort could be used on that road. The only way in which the dangerous *poort* could be traversed was either on horseback or on foot. If a horse was used, it had to be led long distances, and even then it was dangerous if the horse was nervous or frightened. For a considerable distance the footpath ran along a *krans* ledge with the rock face on the one side and a precipice on the other. The first farm to be reached on the plateau is Purekrans, the property of an old well-known inhabitant of Waterberg, the late Mr Piet van Rooyen.

At that time I was the only person in the whole area who could give medical aid of any kind.

On one occasion Mr van Rooyen sent for me as he had suddenly become seriously ill. His son Piet was the bearer of the message. If one is predisposed to believe in premonitions, one would certainly have believed that a fatal outcome to the whole business had been foretold to us by the series of unusual events which preceded it.

On his downward journey, just as he was passing under a huge tree, Piet became aware of a rustling in the branches above him. When he looked up, he saw a large leopard busy hanging up a *duiker* in one of the highest forks of the tree's branches. It had probably just caught the *duiker* and, as is generally known, the leopard has the habit of hanging in trees any captured game which it cannot immediately devour. I had not before heard of anyone who had himself witnessed this scene. Van Rooyen was unarmed, and left the leopard in peace with its prey.

The following day I accompanied Piet on horseback to Purekrans. He was on a large donkey which was accustomed to the path, and I chose the tamest of my horses for the journey.

All went well until, late in the afternoon, we reached the plateau at the northern entrance to Bokpoort. Mr van Rooyen was still in the footpath – by then, of course, on level ground – and he was busy pointing out to me the beauties of that noteworthy area, when our conversation was interrupted by a strange happening.

Suddenly, and to van Rooyen quite unexpectedly, his donkey jumped to one side and at the same time turned its head round until its mouth touched the stirrup. Van Rooyen was quick enough to catch hold of the short mane with one hand, and this saved him from a fall. But his position was not much better than it would have been had he actually fallen. His feet were still in the stirrups, but high in the air where under normal circumstances his head should have been. And there he hung between heaven and earth, with his head downwards while he shouted urgently for help.

The scene was so funny that I am sure van Rooyen himself would have laughed at it if he could have seen it from a safe and more comfortable angle. If perhaps I was inclined to laugh at my friend's dilemma, the desire was speedily smothered when I jumped off my horse to run to his aid, for then I noticed for the first time the terrifying reason for the sudden movement the donkey had so unexpectedly made, and of the strange posture he still maintained.

In the footpath just in front of van Rooyen stood a mamba, erect, with swaying body fiercely angry and ready to strike. The donkey had turned away just far enough to move its own head out of danger, but van Rooyen's position was dangerous enough. His head was not more than a few feet away from the open mouth of the snake, for he was still hanging with his head downwards. If he fell, he would have inevitably fallen almost on top of the deadly creature.

Very slowly and with trembling hands I held van Rooyen and pulled the donkey a little farther away from the snake. I was, of course, on the safe side of the donkey. Then slowly and carefully, I helped van Rooyen back into the saddle.

For some reason the snake did not carry out its threats, and with a sigh of supreme relief I at last saw van Rooyen out of danger.

We then moved carefully with our animals out of the dangerous neighbourhood, while the snake still stood threateningly on guard. When we had got a safe distance away, we began to think of revenge, but in the bare sand flats not a single stone was to be found. We then thought of killing the snake, or, at least, making it innocuous by throwing a stirrup at it.

At best this was a foolish thing to do. Shortly before, an elder brother, Mr Gys van Rooyen, had had a similar encounter with a mamba rolled up in the old wagon road. He had tiptoed round it, but when he was at a safe distance, he also thought of attacking the enemy with stones. With his first shot, which hit the ground an inch from the snake, there was a whirl of dust and a second later the twelve-foot mamba was standing erect before him with his head a few inches from van Rooyen's face.

His presence of mind fortunately did not desert him. For a time, which must have seemed a century to him, he stood dead still without moving a muscle. At last the *makoppa* dropped to the ground again and returned to the place from which he had originally come, and there curled up in the winter sun once more. Mr van Rooyen moved backwards step by step until the mamba was out of sight, and then without molesting it further, he continued his journey.

In our case, the snake tolerated the bombardment with the stirrup without moving, until a shot of mine was so weak that it brought the stirrup to rest a few feet from the snake. We then decided it was better to leave matters as they were, and with the enemy in temporary possession of our weapon we went on our way to Purekrans.

After I had examined Mr van Rooyen, I came to the conclusion that an immediate operation offered the only chance of saving his life. His son and I then returned to Naboomspruit, where unavailingly I tried to get a doctor from one of the larger towns.

At last I got into telegraphic communication with a friend – Dr Corkery of Warmbaths. I explained to him the difficulties of the journey and the critical condition of the patient, and he said immediately that he would come, although he had no experience of horseback riding.

At Naboomspruit Mr van Rooyen and I met him ready for the journey through Bokpoort. I gave Dr Corkery a young mare, slightly nervous, but with this advantage; that she had already been through the *poort* on several occasions. Piet van Rooyen, with the doctor's heavy medical instrument case on the donkey, would lead the procession. I formed the rearguard on a stallion that had also been through the *poort* a number of times. And in this order, we set out on our journey along the footpath.

On my advice Dr Corkery gave the mare free rein, with the result that she walked very slowly, and at times our guide on the donkey got far ahead. There was a dangerous spot in the footpath on the *krans* ledge about which I had said nothing to Dr Corkery. A fall of rock had closed the usual footpath ledge and to circumvent it, we had to make a detour that allowed us to climb to a higher ledge.

Below us was the terrible abyss down to the mountain stream that flowed through the *poort*. The turnout which gave access from the ledge we were on to the one above was about twenty yards along on the south side of the fall of rock which obstructed the old footpath. Just about here van Rooyen got so far ahead on his donkey that for a time he was out of sight. Suddenly he remembered about the turnout, and the possibility that the doctor might unwittingly pass it and ride into the fall of rock on the lower ledge. The path here is so narrow that it would be impossible to turn the horse round. Van Rooyen came back immediately to see what had happened to us and was just in time to witness a most fearful sight.

What he had feared had happened. Dr Corkery allowed his horse to pass the turnout to the upper ledge – about which he, of course, knew nothing. I was about twenty yards behind him and saw that he was taking the wrong road, but too late to prevent him from doing so. It all happened so quickly. I had just called out to the doctor to rein in his horse when the mare saw that she had cornered herself on the narrow ledge. She could not turn round without falling into the chasm.

She began snorting and prancing about while I slipped off alongside my horse to go to the aid of Dr Corkery. I could see he was in immediate and deadly danger. But I was too late to do anything. At the most critical moment, van Rooyen appeared on the upper ledge right above the mare. When she saw the donkey she had been following all day straight above her, the mare lost all control of herself and stood upright against the *krans* face, probably in an attempt to reach the donkey and escape from her misery. But so sudden was her movement and so far over backwards did she move that Dr Corkery fell backwards out of the saddle. Just as I saw him disappear over the edge, the horse too fell over backwards and disappeared from sight.

The noise was terrific. The echoes in the narrow *poort* were enlarged and repeated and repeated again until it seemed like the echoing of a thunderstorm in the mountains. This naturally helped to intensify the awful impression the tragedy had made on me. I was quite certain that horse and rider had been smashed on the rocks below, and the reader can readily imagine with what feelings van Rooyen, when he had reached the lower ledge again, and I hurried to the scene of the accident.

But the hour of Dr Corkery's death had not yet struck. Immediately below the place where he and the horse had fallen down, there was a large fall of rock that had 'calved' out of the *krans* and was wedged against a lower ledge. It formed a sloping table of gravelled stone covered with large patches of *tambotie* grass. On one of these patches Dr Corkery had landed on his back, and next to him, the horse. If the horse had then become restive the incident might still have had a fatal ending. But she was probably wise enough to realise her danger and to lie still, until, with great exertion, we got her on to her legs again. We had to fasten all our reins and halters together to make a rope long enough to fasten her. With this aid, and the use of all our strength, we succeeded at last in getting her on to the footpath ledge again.

Fortune and misfortune seemed to remain in constant balance. When at last we were out of the *poort*, Dr Corkery noticed for the first time that he had lost his spectacles, and he was so near-sighted that he could not possibly operate without glasses. Mr van Rooyen went back immediately to search for the spectacles. We had little hope that he would find them, but he was successful. In one of the clumps of grass where Dr Corkery had fallen, he found the glasses without a scratch on them, and the next day Dr Corkery was able to operate on Mr van Rooyen.

As yet I have told nothing about the baboons of Bokpoort, but I can at least offer the excuse that all these events led to that spectacle.

7
Baboons and Human Beings

SHORTLY AFTER the events I described in the previous chapter, I arrived on horseback, in the company of two old friends I previously mentioned, at the lower entrance to Bokpoort. Both Mr Willem van Staden and Mr Gys van Rooyen had come to Waterberg when the middle-*veld* was one of the great elephant hunting grounds of the Transvaal, and when most of the white inhabitants there made a living out of ivory. What the two old gentlemen did not know about wild animals was scarcely worth learning, and yet that day they witnessed an example of baboon behaviour they would not have believed had they not seen it with their own eyes.

Just below the *poort*, there was a large flat area covered with thorn scrub and criss-crossed by game footpaths, for there was at that time no road and no passage for any sort of vehicle through Bokpoort. Just before we emerged from the thorn scrub, we heard near us the chattering of a troop of baboons. They had obviously not yet become aware of us.

"They are very busy searching for gum," I remember one of the old gentlemen remarked.

To the left ahead of us was a considerable clearing in the bushes. In the middle of it ran the *spruit* (a deep water course which is dry before and after rain) coming from the *poort*. And in that clearing we saw such an extraordinary group that we immediately halted the horses and watched the scene with astonishment for about half an hour. As we were behind the last thorn bushes of the level area, we were invisible to the group.

On the bank of the *spruit* was a small knoll hollowed out on various sides. At one of these hollows there appeared to be about ten young natives, clearly cattle- and goatherds from a nearby *stad*. Some were busy digging pot-clay from the hole with their hands, while others were fashioning oxen and other animals from the clay. Our first impression was that they were all young natives, but we soon noticed that more than half the group consisted of young baboons. A great activity was apparent, and the scramble around the clay hole was so violent that it was the chief reason why we could get so near to them without being discovered.

Baboons and *kaffirs* pushed each other away from the hole in an attempt to get hold of the clay, because the entrance was too narrow to admit more than two at a time reaching the soft clay. From the struggling mass there arose constant laughter, mingled with Sesutu curses of the grossest kind, and above it all, one could hear the jabbering of the baboons.

As soon as a baboon occupied the entrance, he was grabbed by the tail by a little native and dragged backwards, and as soon as a young native was in possession, he was attacked from all sides by the baboons, and so pinched by them that he had to let go his hold of the clay to free himself from his attackers.

Three or four of the older natives did not concern themselves with the struggle. They sat in a circle, each with a large lump of clay beside him on the ground, and between them there was a flat space already filled with the clay oxen and other animals they had made. A portion of this circle also consisted of baboons and they, like the native youths, appeared somewhat older than those at the hole. They sat quietly and sedately, watching with the greatest interest the activities and the completed work of the modellers. Now and again, however, curiosity got the better of one of them. Very quietly and slyly, a hairy hand was stretched out along the

ground to get hold of one of the clay animals. Sometimes the thief succeeded in his attempt, and then the work of art was handed from one baboon to the other and finally broken. When, however, a little native discovered the attempt at theft, he quickly frustrated it by smacking the baboon in the face with a lump of clay. This always caused a terrific uproar. But it was all regarded as a huge joke. Neither natives nor baboons ever became really cross, and the struggling never degenerated into a real fight.

The antics of the smaller natives and baboons around the clay-hole were also very funny. The young natives attempted, of course, to get the clay for a specific purpose. As soon as one had gathered a good lump, he handed it to the modellers. But in the baboons such an objective was lacking. As soon as one got a handful of clay, its main activity was directed towards getting rid of the sticky mess. With great difficulty it removed the stuff from one hand to find it sticking as closely to the other.

There is nothing that makes a baboon so nervous and shudder as having something sticky on its hands. It was a regular joke to hand out honey to the members of our tame troop and then to watch the dance that followed as they tried unavailingly to clean their hands by rubbing them together. Finally, they would rub their hands violently in the sand. Despite all their cleverness, our troop had never learned to use water for this simple purpose. And this type of behaviour we saw at the clay hole, too.

My old friends laughed so much that they could scarcely remain on their horses. Natives and baboons alike were bespattered with clay, and the baboons had it mostly on their faces. One can hardly imagine how extremely funny a little baboon can appear when its face is packed with clay.

This little game came to an unexpected end. All this time the little ones were at the clay hole, they were completely separated from the large ones. These we could still hear occasionally in the trees on our right hand, so that we were between the little ones and the main troop.

When the fun was at its highest at the clay hole I saw indistinctly through the trees to the right a large black form coming directly towards us. It was a surprisingly large male baboon – probably the single leader of a troop, and he had come to see what had happened to the little ones. We became aware of each other simultaneously. Only once did it give utterance, and that in a roaring voice to give a baboon warning. Then it disappeared as speedily as it had come.

The effect on the group at the clay hole showed us how complete was the understanding and association between the little natives and the baboons. Both understood at once this warning notice of extreme alarm, and both knew that it meant grave peril. Without even looking to see from where the danger threatened, the baboons and little *kaffirs* scattered in opposite directions – the *kaffirs* back to the *stad* and the little baboons to the large troop in the thorn bush. The baboons had to pass within a few yards in front of us, and their comical appearance again made my two old friends roar with laughter.

But soon all other feelings were surpassed by our wonderment at what we had seen. Again and again Mr Van Staden exclaimed, "I've seen today what I've never seen in my life before. If someone had told me about it I would never have believed him."

We called at the little *stad* to make further inquiries about this unusual incident. Here we learnt from the old natives that the troop had never been fired at since, and even before, the Anglo-Boer War. In time the baboons had become so impudent, so cheeky, that they often stole mealies and pumpkins from the roofs of the straw huts, while the owners were still sitting inside. The old natives knew that the herd boys had made playmates of the little baboons. They had been forbidden to do so and had been punished on various occasions for disobeying. "But it doesn't help," said the old foreman of the *stad* in a despondent voice. "They go out of their way and leave the goats and cattle in the *veld* to be able to go and play with the baboons."

8
Reason in Apes and
Lower Species of Animal

IT IS ALWAYS A SOURCE of wonderment to me to read what can be written by most popular 'animal writers' about the psychology of animals, and which is accepted as the truth by their readers.

In one of the issues of the well-known English periodical *The Strand* there appeared a series of stories about cats which the compiler offered as evidence of their intelligence. He stated among other things that the cat learns to do 'tricks' without being taught and on its own initiative; whereas the ape, among other animals, can be taught such tricks only with much trouble.

The reader must deduce from this that the cat is in certain respects the possessor of a more human intelligence than the ape! He tells the following cat story, communicated by a highly respected lady correspondent.

A certain cat always received its food in a plate on the floor. This cat came from an aristocratic family, in which all the manners and behaviour of high nobility were inborn. At the house next door there was a cat from the common stock with which the 'lord' would have nothing to do. There was never any association or meeting between them.

On one occasion, the mistress placed a plate of food before the 'lord', but in the meantime he had smelt something cooking in the kitchen; he would rather have that than his usual food. He sat and looked at the plate of food without putting his lips to it. His mistress knew at once what was going on in his mind, and said to the cat, "You will get nothing else until you have eaten everything in front of you." And what did the wonderful cat do?

It immediately paid a visit to the 'street' cat, which it had always formerly treated with the greatest contempt, and a few moments later it walked in, followed by the strange cat which had never before been near the house. He led the visitor to the plate of food and encouraged it, in the presence of his mistress, to eat the undesired course – which the visitor speedily did.

I do not think there is a South African child of ten that would accept this as truth.

Never was there an animal under the wide expanse of heaven below the intellectual level of man which could reason in that way. A cat that could do that could be taught to read and write.

All domesticated animals which have been associated with man for generations have evolved a higher and more human-like intelligence than the wild species of the same race of forest and *veld*. But the cleverest dog in the world could not reason in that way, and the dog stands in the same relation to the cat, as far as intelligence is concerned, as man does to the ape. The anthropoid apes come next to man in reasoning ability, but I doubt whether the cleverest chimpanzee could master such a chain of cause and effect. I would never dream of expecting anything like this from a baboon, and to compare the reasoning ability of an ape with that of a cat is like placing the intelligence of a university professor on the same level as that of a Kalahari Bushman.

The article in *The Strand* made me think of telling a few ape stories and of comparing the 'reasoning' which ordinary apes and baboons exhibit with the most outstanding power of reasoning in cats.

To take the simplest of matters that baboons can do in captivity – behaviour which most South Africans have seen. There is, for instance, the example of the baboon that every night carries its bag to its sleeping box to use it as a covering. Every baboon does that regularly on its own initiative where the opportunity occurs. Would a cat ever be able to do anything like that – for instance, to pull a small cushion from a chair and sleep on it, or anything like it? Merely to put the question is enough to show that such behaviour cannot be imagined.

I go a step farther. During Dr Gunning's time the baboons in the State Zoo at Pretoria were tied to poles. There was a stream of water just within the reach of some, but not of all. A few could reach the water with their hands, but not with their lips. Each baboon had its little milk tin, and all those chained too shortly had learnt by themselves, as a matter of daily habit, to dish water from the furrow with their tins, and so to slake their thirst.

Some old cross-patched individuals usually threw anything they could lay hands on at native spectators, but they never used their tins for this purpose. Some of them even carried out a deeply laid plan. They kept the tin full of water close at hand, and as soon as a *kaffir* came near, they threw the water at him. They never dared to behave in this way towards a European. Imagine a cat which could by any conceivable means think out and execute such a simple series of actions. It would immediately be world-famous.

The chimpanzee, Joe, showed an unabating antipathy towards *kaffirs*. During the time he was tied up outside, he was just able to throw a stone at some of them, and he would sometimes keep a little store of stones for hours until he could at last throw one at a native. When, afterwards, there were no more stones to be found in his neighbourhood, he collected gravel and sand in heaps and used that as ammunition. But the natives got to know him and took care to watch him from a safe distance.

As he could not reach them with sand, he devised another plan. With great patience, he dug lumps of gravel from the hard soil. As soon as he had a little heap of sand and gravel together, he would take it in both hands and blow through the opening between the thumbs. In this way he blew away all the dust, and the rubble and small stones remained. This was then carefully stored in a heap. If he had time, he would carefully sort out all the larger stones from the heap of gravel and gather these again into a separate heap. If by some pretence of unconcern he could cleverly lure a *kaffir* within range, his rejoicing and delight was unbounded as he threw the handful of little stones into the native's face.

When he was caged he still occasionally, from behind the wire-netting, threw the remains in his drinking tin at natives, and sometimes he also used as ammunition a substance which should remain nameless, but which was effective enough. It was noteworthy that he never used this substance if he knew beforehand that it could not go through the somewhat fine mesh of the wire of his cage. For his purpose, it had to be almost liquid. (As far as decency and cleanliness are concerned, his behaviour left much to be desired.) If the desired water in his tin was missing, he supplied the necessary fluid in another way, so that he might greet some over-curious *kaffir* with it.

Now think of the cat in connection with behaviour of this nature and compare the statement of the writer in *The Strand* – that cats learn 'tricks' by themselves which apes can learn only with difficulty – with this behaviour. If you allowed a tin at the end of a string to sink a thousand times into otherwise unattainable drinking water in front of a dog or a cat, is there a cat or a dog yet born that would attempt to imitate the action? Any other animal, too, would die of thirst beside the water before using the simplest utensils placed within its reach for obtaining water. But a wild baboon would immediately use the utensil on the string even if it had never seen its use before.

There is no difference perceptible in kind between the intelligence of the baboon and the chimpanzee – it is only a matter of degree.

In Europe I had for a time in my care a young chimpanzee, and I could easily write a book of examples of behaviour which the most extravagant admirer of domestic animals would have to admit as proofs of an intelligence that lies beyond the horizon of such animals and, in fact, of any other species of animal except the primates.

I remember one of the chimpanzee's tricks which will give the reader an idea of how far its reasoning powers extended.

When it was still very small, it was allowed to roam loose in the house – as long as I was present. In the window sill, where it could sit quietly for hours, it could gain infinite enjoyment from watching the passing traffic. At that time, too, I had the previously mentioned South American ape, one of the smallest kind in the world. A great friendship speedily sprang up between the marmoset and the chimpanzee, and as long as I was present they would play and romp together for hours on end, notwithstanding the fact that the chimpanzee could almost fold its little playmate up in one hand. But the fondling and the pranks of the chimpanzee were too rough for the little ape, so I never risked leaving them together during my absence. The marmoset was regularly locked in a canary cage – the door of which had to be locked with quite a complicated arrangement. There was a metal pin attached to a chain which had first to be pulled out before the slot could be withdrawn. Then the slot had to be turned before it could be pushed out. I do not think the chimpanzee had watched the manipulation of this complicated arrangement five times before it could open it as adroitly as I could to free the marmoset.

As protection for the little ape, I hung the cage from the ceiling on a chain above the table, out of reach of the chimpanzee. But for safety's sake, I watched them through a window because I was not quite sure that the marmoset was safe. And this is what I saw.

The chimpanzee had a high baby chair on wheels, in which it sat at the table. It climbed onto the table and tried fruitlessly to reach the cage with outstretched arms. Then it got down and pushed the baby chair against the table and struggled a great deal to get the chair onto the table, but the arms of the chair kept hooking below the table top. The chimpanzee gazed at it for a while and then got down and turned the chair with its back to the table. Then it was fairly easy to drag the chair up. But it soon saw that it would be of little help while the chair lay flat on the table.

After further struggling, it succeeded in getting the baby chair onto its wheels. But still it could not reach the cage. For a while it tried to get one of the dining room chairs (a heavy one) onto the table, and then apparently gave up the whole business as fruitless, although only six inches was left between the hand and the cage. But this baffled it for a long time, and I was about to leave when I saw the last proof of its unusual intelligence.

In my room, on a rack, I kept a little canister – about two feet high – in which were stored biscuits for the little ape. I had taught the chimpanzee the difficult trick of opening the canister with a key which it had first to fetch out of a drawer. When it had given up the struggle with the large chair, it disappeared from the room, and a few moments later I heard a clatter on the stairs, and then the chimpanzee appeared with the biscuit tin which it alternately pushed and pulled. It had obviously rolled it down the stairs. This tin it lifted on to a chair next to the table. Then it got on to the table and pulled the canister up by the handle. It was then placed, with much trouble, on the seat of the baby chair, and a minute later the marmoset was on the chimpanzee's shoulder.

If one analyses step by step the reasoning that motivates such behaviour and then compares it with the behaviour of the cleverest cat or dog the world has seen, one cannot even put the question whether the thinking powers of these species of animals are of the same kind.

But it is not only association with human beings that enables apes to evolve this type of intelligence. In many respects, our wild troop of baboons showed the same type of intelligence – most certainly in a lesser degree – but in its nature there was no difference.

9
Law and Government among the Baboons

WHEN THE TROOP OF BABOONS on Doornhoek had become so tame that we could study them from fairly close at hand, we made a number of discoveries. Most of them were previously quite unknown to me, and some of them came as an astonishing surprise.

It was not the cleverness and the human-like intelligence of the baboon in his natural environment that surprised me most. As far as that was concerned, we naturally expected a great deal because, like most South Africans, we were acquainted with the behaviour and habits of baboons in captivity, and we knew well enough that it was cleverer and could reason more effectively than any lower animal in Africa. On the other hand, it is true we learnt for the first time some of the 'reasonable' habits of the troop which were indeed noteworthy, and which in many instances struck visitors – more especially foreign zoologists – as almost unbelievable wonders. But nonetheless, it was not in this direction that our surprise and curiosity were especially aroused.

What struck me first of all, and most strongly, was the fact that beyond all doubt, we were here in touch with matters which in their more complete development in man were known by high-sounding names. At first hazily and ill-defined, but later more clearly and more obviously, we noticed in the baboon troop 'laws', 'order', 'government', 'culture' – or whatever we may wish to call that which more definitely distinguishes human from animal society.

To speak of 'morals' among baboons may give rise to a smile in most people, and yet it is certain that without the observance of certain fixed 'moral' laws, they could not exist a week. This is so with all gregarious animals. The existence of the troop was possible only because of the observance of certain laws. Among lower animals they are more difficult to discover and attest with certainty, but in the baboon troop they are more obviously apparent because the baboon's behaviour has a more human quality.

The first fact in connection with 'government' of which we became aware in our troop was the existence of a definite leadership.

As a result of that biological knowledge which is almost the heritage of those living in a land so teeming with animal life, we naturally expected something of the sort. We knew at least that tame animals – sheep and goats, for instance – were often led by a special individual, usually a castrated ram, and that for sheep, a leading goat was often kept for no other purpose than to lead the flock. We also knew that among 'wild' Afrikaner cattle, an old bull was in most cases the leader of the troop, and no other individual would attempt to rob him of this honour. Hunters have also found that among wild gregarious animals, there is usually a special leader or leaders. Among elephants, this special function is entrusted to a *poenskop* cow (a cow without tusks). In all other gregarious African animals, the leader or leaders are, without exception, males.

Our first meeting with the leaders of our troop took place when we distributed food – a method we adopted as the first step towards taming the baboons. At first every evening we placed dried mealies on the rocks in the vicinity of the sleeping place, and when the baboons had become accustomed to this, the mealies were always strewn in the grass nearer to the huts. The baboons were very suspicious at first, and very careful. If the

mealies were somewhat too near the huts to their liking, the older ones definitely refused to be enticed. In a large semicircle they sat motionless on the rocks, and carefully watched all our coming and going from a safe distance.

As in many other instances, the little ones were the most impetuous. They were always prepared to approach fifty or sixty feet nearer than the old ones. Here they indulged in all sorts of pranks which clearly had the motive of enticing us to reveal our intentions.

They were always prepared to turn anything into a prank or joke. One of these games was to run suddenly towards us in a huddled mass, as though they were quite unafraid and wanted immediately to make booty of the heap of mealies. But despite all the appearance of fearlessness, it was funny to see how, during the advance towards us, the one would hide behind the other. As soon as they reached a point they regarded as dangerous, a halt was called, and a silly sort of dance was performed. This consisted of jumping up and down with stiff outstretched arms and legs, which at the same time were waved up and down.

If that produced no movement from our side (which naturally was always the case), one after the other the baboons would make the most insulting gesture known in baboon behaviour. It is a sign which anyone who has kept watch for some time on baboons knows well, and to which the baboons can give several widely divergent meanings, each of which is determined by circumstances and is indicated by small differences of attitude. On these occasions, however, it was purely insulting, mocking, and provocative.

It is performed with the back turned towards the object of the gesture, but our little ones always looked slyly through their legs to see what effect the 'challenge' would have. If nothing happened, they walked back to the circle of older ones with stiff legs and tails erect. If attitude and gesture could say anything, then without doubt this gesture meant, "We are not afraid of you and, moreover, you are worth nothing".

The fearlessness of the little ones increased daily, and here we saw the first proof of a regular 'government'. We noticed that there was a group of particularly large old males which always remained together, and usually at a distance from the large troop. The number of these was later fixed at eleven.

At night (of course at the beginning of our acquaintance) while the little ones were up to their pranks, the small group was always the farthest away from us. There they sat motionless together, assuming an attitude as if we were the last thing visible within the limits of their horizon in which they had any interest. There was, however, a continuous soft mumbling among them which sounded so much like human talk that often we were almost convinced that the baboons were capable of articulated speech. Our natives implicitly believed that they were.

It always seemed as if the older ones never took any notice whatever of the play of the little ones, until on one occasion the little ones came nearer to the huts than they had ever been before. Suddenly there was a *basso-profundo* shout by one member of the old council and immediately, without a moment's delay, without looking at us again, the little ones rushed up to the circle of older ones. Each one immediately went to its mother.

There was a moment's silence; then from the same old baboon came a deep bass grumble, and immediately the whole troop began to move. They did not run, they walked slowly away from us, every mother with her baby on her back, towards the sleeping place, and in the lead was the same 'council of eleven', which by then already had a certain identity for us.

There was no doubt about the meaning of those two sounds. The first was a command to the little ones to return immediately, the second a command to the whole troop to trek to the sleeping place, or at least to get on the move and follow the eleven leaders.

Subsequently, we heard them hundreds of times, and in time came to the conclusion that we had here not mere leaders of a troop, but with a special form of government which did not occur in any other species of animal in Africa.

In consequence, we paid special attention at first to the behaviour of our council of eleven, and also collected information from all possible quarters about the leadership in other wild troops of baboons in Waterberg. We finally came to the conclusion that, as far as numbers are concerned, the government of the troops varies widely.

In many cases, without regard to the size of the troop, there was undoubtedly a single leader and ruler. From Mr Emil Tamsen I learnt that on his well-known fruit farm near Nylstroom, there was a troop of baboons under the government of a single leader.

On one occasion his son succeeded in shooting and killing this leader with the immediate consequence that the whole troop became disorganised. Until then they had all followed their leader and obeyed his commands, with the result that it was very difficult to get a shot at them when they were marauding. The leader always led them safely out of all traps and away from all obstacles. When he died, however, the troop was so disorganised and dismayed that they could not even flee, and a large number of them were shot before they could reach safety.

On Swagershoek, the farm of Mr Andries van Heerden, I had the opportunity of watching from near at hand a troop of baboons for a long time. Their nightly habitation was a beautiful little cave in a *krans* directly opposite the house. And never before did I see a troop that was so troubled by leopards. Almost every night we could follow the whole tragedy step by step from the *stoep* of Mr van Heerden's house.

Night after night the troop was ambushed. The actual attack of the leopard could be singled out by the anguished cry of the victim. This sound was followed immediately by the angry roar of the large males, and often from the house we could see them sally out in battle array against their arch-enemy.

The leopard, of course, was invisible. From that point the sequence of events was always the same. After their unsuccessful pursuit of the leopard we could see the troop returning to the cave with a persistent lamentation. The groaning and begging of the wounded animal which had been paralysed by a single bite of the leopard before the latter had fled for its own life would persist.

Then later, when night had swathed the mountains completely in her mantle of darkness, we could hear the muffled growling of the leopard on its way back to its unfortunate victim to give it its quietus. After escaping, the leopard first went to drink from a dam at the foot of the mountain and then, at its leisure, returned to fetch its victim.

Its stealthy creeping towards the wounded baboon usually evoked a last cry of agony and terror which the troop always greeted with a thundering roar from the entrance of the sleeping place. But the courage of the bravest baboon was never proof against darkness and the enemy together. They could do no more than roar and threaten. One could hear clearly how the leopard leapt upon its prey with a savage roar – and after that the eternal silence of the hills slowly covered the world.

On several occasions, Mr van Heerden and I tried to lie in wait for the leopard as it returned from its visit to the dam, but we soon learnt that far greater preparation than we had made was necessary if we wished to catch the slyest animal that lives in, as it were, a trap of its own making.

I think that this nightly tragedy aroused some feeling of sympathy in Mr van Heerden towards his baboons. In any case, he was the only Waterberg farmer in my experience who had a good word for baboons, and they gave him, heaven knows, enough reason for vengeance. But when the question was discussed of using a discovery by which it was possible to poison the whole troop at once, Mr van Heerden said decisively that he would not make use of that remedy.

"I don't mind having a pot at them now and then, but to kill the whole lot together is another matter. And besides, I would miss my old pals terribly."

When I was there, there was also a single leader of this troop. He had many strange and funny habits. One of them was to come down to the mealie fields – first, and alone. He picked a single mealie and then went to an open patch in the land where he sat down and devoured it. From this open patch he had a view of the homestead and all entrances to the mealie fields. When he had satisfied himself that all was safe, he made a single sound which immediately called the troop down from the mountain and invited them to the feast. But as long as he did not give the command, the troop would not move. If the leader noticed anything that aroused his suspicions at the house, he calmly ate the mealie without calling down his followers. Then he plucked a second mealie and so repeated the performance. Sometimes he returned to the troop satisfied without having called his subjects – as long as the danger at the house was still noticeable.

This behaviour had come about no doubt as the result of a long series of attempts by Mr van Heerden to catch the 'Old President'. The experience gained by Mr van Heerden during these attempts established certain facts we had previously proved experimentally in our tame troop.

He became certain, as I had, that there is no question of the knowledge of numbers in the baboon. The old contention, constantly repeated, that the baboon can count to two but not to three, has repeatedly been disproved experimentally by me, and here on Mr van Heerden's farm we proved again that the contention is based on an error.

What *is* true, however, is that the baboon knows every member of the human household with which it has constant association. It knows which are the dangerous and which the harmless ones in the house. If ten of the inhabitants of the house go out to the land, and only two are dangerous, the baboons will give all their attention to the two. If one of the dangerous ones returns to the house, the baboons will still stay away: but if both go back, the baboons will come down, even though the other eight harmless humans are still there.

In Swagershoek, Mrs van Heerden inspired no fear in the baboons. If her husband rode away from the house, the troop was in the mealie fields in a few minutes. Even the presence of Mrs van Heerden in the land did not frighten them away. With the greatest impudence, they stole mealies a few yards away from her. They treated a group of women and children with exactly the same contempt.

This suggested to us a plan which we carried out at once. Mr van Heerden, dressed in one of his wife's frocks and with his gun carefully concealed beneath it, walked into the lands with Mrs van Heerden. The baboons made a row in the mountains, but not a single one came down within gunshot.

I had forecast that the attempt would be unsuccessful, because I knew how unbelievably sharp the sight and how very keen the attention of the baboon could be. Mrs van Heerden then came home alone, while her husband hid in the land. But still the baboons did not leave the mountains.

Mr van Heerden then returned, and when he (still disguised in woman's clothing) and his wife went to the land for a second time, and he returned alone, he had scarcely reached the house when the troop was in the land.

Once, at the request of Mr van Heerden, I played a mean trick on the 'Old President'. I must say it went against the grain, and I was pleased that the incident ended without bloodshed.

On his reconnoitring trips to the land, the old leader had a keen eye for a gun. Although the distance was six hundred yards, the appearance of a man with a gun at the house was always sufficient to make him flee.

One day when he was sitting on his usual open patch spying out the land and busy with a stolen mealie, I stalked him from behind the house and was careful to show only enough of my face to enable me to get a good aim at him. I had a Mannlicher mauser of very fine calibre and hard bullets, so I fostered the hope that even if by chance I hit it, the wound would most probably not be deadly. The 'Old President' was enormous, and when the rifle was sighted on him, he seemed more like a gorilla to me than a baboon.

As the shot fired, he rolled over backwards violently and the mealie flew into the air. We all thought it was a deadly shot, but I heaved a sigh of relief when I saw him jump up and run towards the mountain where his subjects had in the meantime greeted my effort with the greatest anger and a good deal of noise. The greater part of the troop rushed to meet him and concernedly surrounded him. We could see him sitting encircled by his subjects, high in the mountain, while he attentively watched us at the house.

With gun in hand, I immediately went to the land, followed later by Mr van Heerden. There was no drop of blood on his spoor, but at the place where he had fallen over there was a bunch of that long hair which sometimes grows on the head of old males between the ears. It was a narrow escape indeed for the Old President.

It was noteworthy that the leader never undertook another reconnoitring journey to the land as long as I was staying at the house.

The question may be asked: how did we establish the existence of 'laws' and 'government' among baboons? They cannot of course, talk, there is no written 'constitution'. The existence of such must then, as in the case of all other natural characteristics of animals below man in mental development, be deduced only from their behaviour.

As soon as we began to know the troop individually, we could establish with certainty that there were eleven large old males which made, more or less, a single group. When the baboons were on trek, one could not easily distinguish them from the rest. But as soon as there was the slightest disturbance which temporarily stopped the trek, the eleven were somewhere in the vanguard together. It happened so quickly that it was difficult to determine whether they had a definite arrangement: that is, whether one of the eleven was in every case the rallying point of this sudden congregation.

One thing was certain, however; there was absolute equality among the eleven. There was never a fight, and never the least sign of disunity. Fights between other members of the troop occurred fairly frequently, but never between members of the 'council'. Sexual rivalry is the usual cause of duels in all species of animals, but in our troop nothing of this sort occurred, though I have reason to believe that it is not so in all troops.

This brings us to the consideration of that form of sexual behaviour which was the rule in our troop during our association with it.

Usually males and females were equal in numbers. There were always a number of young males without mates. As soon as a female became sexually mature there was usually a certain amount of competition. Often, however, competition was completely absent.

In such cases a sort of understanding arose between a young male and a female (before she had reached sexual maturity). For a week or two beforehand, the two were constantly together. The awakening of first love was clearly perceptible. The young male in most cases showed his love by constant and untiring search in the hair of his beloved. If he brought back more than one mealie from a raid he silently allowed her to take one from under his arm – an act which not another one in the troop would have dared. He would turn over stones for her and sit watching as she took away insects from in front of him. At night they slept together with their arms round each other. In such cases there was never any competition from other males. When the female had in this way clearly indicated her choice, the marriage was accepted by the whole troop as an accomplished fact.

Not one of our males had more than one wife, but I think that was because the sexes were always equal. In troops where there are more females than males, polygamy was the rule. With us this never occurred, or at least there was always a doubt as to whether what appeared to be a case of polygamy really was one. And this was due to the fact that conjugal infidelity often occurred.

As far as my experience goes, I have never seen a male attempt to rob by force the acknowledged wife of another, or to steal it by making love to it. But it often happened that an old female fell in love with a young male before the latter had acquired a wife. In such a case the old female always tried in the slyest way to lure the baboon Joseph to her immoral purposes, and her victim was never proof against the temptations of Potiphar's wife.

The unfaithful female had to be very careful, for if her true husband caught her red-handed, he punished her and her lover with the utmost rigour of baboon law. After he had thoroughly trounced his wife, he would turn his attention to her gallant, who usually took good care to flee before the punishment of the wife had been completed. But this early flight did not save him; the furious husband followed him with unrelenting persistence until he caught him, and then the punishment was usually violent. A pursuit of this kind often lasted for weeks on end. Every time the two met, the anger of the dishonoured husband would flare up anew, so that the existence of the young gigolo frequently became a martyrdom.

The wife, however, was never punished more than once, but it was noteworthy that she did not regain the full confidence of her husband for months. He kept her in sight constantly, and even to see her in the neighbourhood of her former lover was enough to make him rail furiously at the young male.

But it did not always happen that the dishonoured husband immediately discovered the unfaithfulness of his spouse. An unlawful love affair lasted sometimes for months if the husband was unusually stupid and especially at ease. It was such cases which during our early acquaintance with the troop we regarded as polygamy.

The quiet wedding of the two which had fallen in love before sexual maturity was not a regular rule among our troop. In just as many cases, two or three young males simultaneously courted a young female which had reached maturity. If that happened, the female always pretended coyness and ran away with her lovers in a string behind her. There was never any violence or fighting. The race sometimes lasted for a whole day, until all were so tired that they could do no more than struggle along at a trot.

What I found most strange in this behaviour was that young baboons during these periods of love-madness often lost all their usual fear of man and their carefulness. I know of cases where three or four such love-racers, without the least sign of fear or fright, ran through a group of people at the homestead. Usually it was the people who got the fright. I know of cases where ladies on a footpath near the farmhouse had been touched glancingly by baboons on their love-run. I know of cases where baboons in love had been mistaken for ghosts in the evening twilight, and the farm acquired a reputation (which it has never shaken) of being haunted.

As soon as the female was so weary that she could continue no farther, she immediately and clearly indicated her choice; and from such a choice there is no appeal in baboon law. Without the least opposition the disappointed lovers accepted her decision. Quite calmly, they walked home together to the sleeping place which they reached in the pitch dark with the possibility that a leopard might crown the end of their race with slaughter. The married pair came home alone and from that moment their marriage was acknowledged and respected by the troop.

It was not always the winner of the race who was chosen. Often the offer of the winner – perhaps a large strong male – was refused in favour of a weaker competitor. That is why the they persisted to the end, no matter how far behind they might be left. It is a remarkable fact, and one about which there cannot be the least doubt, that the females can always run faster and keep up longer than the males.

Every member of the council had one wife, and among them, as also among the very old baboons of the troop, there was unbroken conjugal fidelity.

The females have certain rights which are scrupulously upheld by the whole troop. The males must protect and defend them in all circumstances. If danger threatens, the full-grown males form a vanguard, and they will often sacrifice their lives to prevent an assault on the females and little ones.

The wife is always entitled to a share of the food her husband gathers. If he discovers a tree or plant with ripe fruit, he will lead his wife to it, and though he himself does not eat, he keeps others away while she enjoys the discovered food. If he raids a land while she, from fear, remains in the mountain he will, on his return, hand over to her a share of the mealies or fruit, or rather will allow her to take it from him.

Assistance given by the male to the female extends further, and in one respect it helps to place the character of the baboon in a better light and to make him more attractive. As soon as the baby of any pair is so big that it moves from its mother's breast to her back, it is the male who carries it in all difficult places. If there is a sudden alarm and the troop must flee, it is the husband who grabs the baby and carries it out of danger. The mother is so confident that she can trust her husband to the death in this respect that she often flees without troubling about her child.

But the behaviour of the male is even nobler as regards the other infants of the troop. He will, of course, always attempt to save his own child first, but after that he is always ready to offer his life in defence of the other little ones of the troop. If the alarm comes suddenly and the danger is pressing, every large male will grab the child nearest to him regardless of whether it is his own or not.

In the protection and the carrying of the little ones, in the general defence of the troop, the council of eleven were always first and in the forefront. Their office was certainly no sinecure. If danger came, they ran first to meet it and they were the last to retreat. And this is the case with all leaders of troops.

10
Death among Baboons

ONE UNUSUALLY DARK NIGHT, about midnight, we were awakened by unusual sounds around the huts. I remember I was just busy lighting the lantern when I became aware of a large dark hand against the window pane, and immediately thereafter saw the silhouette of a black form. It was so dark outside that I could not make out what it was. In the very faint starlight, moreover, all black and dark objects were doubled in size.

Shortly afterwards, I heard Mr Austin calling out from the adjoining hut. He, too, did not know what was happening. We had just dressed when we heard the natives at their huts calling to each other, and above all the voices, the voice of our baboon expert, Johannesburg. "Don't throw! Don't throw stones!" he called out in warning and repeatedly, clearly to the other natives.

When we got outside with the lantern, we saw to our amazement that we were surrounded by large baboons. One after the other, they appeared in the light of the lantern and then disappeared again in the darkness. It took a little while before we recognised them as our council of leaders. Our astonishment was due to the fact that we have never before seen anything like this, and we had thus far been under the impression that baboons were so afraid of the dark that not a single one would willingly have left the sleeping place during the night. We found out later that this belief was not always correct. However, the behaviour of the baboons that night was so strange and unusual that its cause was a mystery to us.

They were all perfectly quiet. We soon discovered that only seven or eight of the leaders were present. There was no sign of anxiety or excitement. Almost all the time, they sat in silence without any sign that they were interested in what we were doing. But we knew enough about baboon behaviour by then to know that, as is usual with baboons, they kept us constantly in sight without directly looking at us. That something was amiss was certain, but what could it be?

There came no sound from the sleeping place. A deathly silence reigned over the whole *kloof.* It could obviously not be a leopard, because the appearance of their arch-enemy in the *kloof* was, without exception, accompanied by a terrific noise – a noise with which we were all acquainted and which was easily distinguishable. The secret stillness of the huge males struck me most – this, coupled perhaps with the inky darkness of the night that limited our horizon to a few yards.

Johannesburg thought that something was amiss at the sleeping place, but he could not explain the reason for this nocturnal visit and the secret silence. His experience was limited to the behaviour of baboons during the day. In Blouberg, in the days of his youth, he had never made acquaintance with baboons during the night, for if there is one being more afraid of the dark than a baboon, it is a young native.

At last we decided to visit the sleeping place. We had seen the return home of the troop that evening and watched them climb into the sleeping place after we had distributed half a bag of mealies to them. It was a time of great drought, and in consequence, food was extremely scarce. Mealies were so scarce and dear that we had to cut the ration to a minimum. Nonetheless, we felt certain that it could not be hunger and the accompanying desire for food that caused this unusual behaviour.

On the way to the sleeping place, I walked ahead with the

lantern. On either side we were accompanied by the large males which had come to visit us. Usually the appearance of the light of our lantern in the middle of the night would have caused considerable upheaval at the sleeping place, but when we got to the rocks below it, everything was still and deathly quiet.

Here the other members of the council also made their appearance. They were not on the sleeping place, but they had been keeping watch on the tops of the highest rocks in the narrow *kloof*. When we approached, they came down as though they expected our arrival. The only sound we heard then was the whispered mumbling of one or two males.

I can still remember the impression the scene made on me. The wild rocks shadowed by dark rock-growth, the large uncertain black forms gathered around us, the flickering light of the lantern, and, above all, the unearthly silence – all combined to give an eerie sensation which was closely related to fear if it was not actually fear itself, although we were both armed with rifles and mauser pistols.

In time the apparent apathy of the baboons made us feel more at ease, and when we had discussed the matter from all angles, we neared the sleeping place itself.

I have previously explained that the sleeping place was a deep hollow in the *krans* covered in front by a large wild fig tree. An entrance to the sleeping place was provided by a sloping fall of rock which reached from the floor of the *kloof* to the lowest branches of the wild fig tree.

I also explained that the sleeping baboons would never permit us to set foot on the floor of their den during the night. They would allow us to come only as far as the branches of the fig tree. As soon as we tried to approach nearer, the members of the council would come forward with such a threatening bearing, that we knew well that another step forward would invite an attack that would place our lives in the greatest danger. That is why we never visited the sleeping place at night. During the day we could visit and examine it carefully, for during the day the baboons were never there.

On this night, however, we experienced one of the few exceptions in this respect.

When we reached the branches of the fig tree, the large males, one after the other, got up to the sleeping place by way of the rocks. Their bearing was so quiet and peaceable that we finally dared to get down on the floor and to approach the troop from a distance.

As usual, they were gathered into a tight ball, the males on the outside and the females and weaned little ones in the middle. We could see the little curious eyes of the infants now and then shine out in the lantern light as they climbed on to the females to watch us interestedly over the heads of the large ones. But they too were quiet – something so unusual that it strengthened the impression that we were in the presence of some great tragedy about which the males had tried to tell us, but which we could not decipher.

For a whole hour, we watched the troop on the sleeping place carefully, but could not discover the cause of their behaviour. It was not only that the baboons in this huddled mass were silent – they made no actual movement. With bent heads tucked beneath their arms, not one of the large ones made any effort to look at the unusual visitors and the lantern light. The members of the council remained apart from the troop, and gave the impression that they were keeping watch between us and the circle.

We had to leave the place no wiser than when we arrived.

We were, however, as certain as we could be of anything on earth that something serious had happened, and that the baboons had visited us in the night to tell us about it, and to ask for our help – and we could not understand each other.

*

On the following day, just before daybreak, we were again awakened by the baboons. When we came out of the huts, the natives had already gathered in a group to listen to the sounds that came from the sleeping place. It was at once noticeable that the natives were deeply moved by the sound of lamentation – something we noticed on more than one occasion thereafter.

What we heard was the terrible blood-freezing cry of woe from the baboons – persistent and heart-rending. It is almost impossible to exaggerate the effect of this sound on the human being. On most occasions it sounded, to our ears, more moving than even the cry of mourning of human beings, just because the lamentation of the baboons is wordless. It is a purely emotional sound, more or less similar to the inarticulate groaning and sighing by which the deepest anguish of the human heart finds speechless expression.

We immediately went to the sleeping place, where the secret of the whole matter was speedily revealed.

Below the *krans* on the floor of the narrow *kloof*, lay the corpses of about eight weaned young ones which had died during the night and had been cast out, as the troop usually does with all its dead.

At first I was afraid to handle the little corpses, for over the edge of the *krans* we could see the faces of the large baboons as they interestedly spied on us. A lower animal – a beast of prey, for instance – would in such a case have been tempted to attack. But the intelligence of the baboons came to their aid. They understood well the meaning of death and without any sign of opposition allowed us to remove the bodies to the huts.

Only one unfortunate young mother followed almost on our heels with all kinds of begging sounds, and here we discovered something wonderful. It was not for the return of her child that she was begging, for when we placed all the bodies on the ground in front of her (we could not distinguish her infant from the others) she touched, in a most moving way, her own child with her lips.

But it was only for a few seconds. She did not try to pick up the babe or take away the body. And then almost at once, she sat with her arms stretched out to us continuously and continued her begging.

What did she want? Obviously not the return of her dead infant. But she did want something which, to her dim intelligence, we alone were able to give her. She wanted exactly what the seven large males who had visited us so unexpectedly the previous evening had wanted; our help in warding off the approaching death of the infants – that approaching death of which in all probability they had become aware the previous evening.

And the mother wanted from us the revival of her child. She wanted to have changed that huge and remorseless condition which in her environment she had learnt to know as death. Somewhere in her spirit, the belief must have arisen that these magicians she had learnt to know would perhaps be able to give life back to her child.

It seems far-fetched to imagine something like that about the thinking powers of a baboon, but afterwards we encountered in their behaviour further proof that 'thinking' of this quality was not at all improbable.

The mother followed us to the huts and waited for a long time before hope deserted her.

The death of the infants was due to a form of internal rupture which attacked only the little ones. It was naturally due to the famine which reigned in the mountains as a result of the drought. The chief symptom was inflammation of the gums which made the eating of hard food impossible, and the babies had in consequence died of exhaustion.

THE END

Made in the USA
Las Vegas, NV
05 May 2023

71598596R00177